Kunststofftechnik

Filtration of polymer melts

Published by Verein Deutscher Ingenieure
VDI-Gesellschaft Kunststofftechnik

English translation by M. S. Welling

VDI-Verlag GmbH
Verlag des Vereins Deutscher Ingenieure · Düsseldorf

CIP-Kurztitelaufnahme der Deutschen Bibliothek

Filtration of polymer melts / publ. by Verein
Dt. Ingenieure, VDI-Ges. Kunststofftechnik. –
Düsseldorf: VDI-Verlag, 1981.
    (Kunststofftechnik)
    Dt. Ausg. u. d. T.: Filtrieren von Kunststoff-
    schmelzen
    ISBN 3-18-404081-X

NE: Gesellschaft Kunststofftechnik

© VDI-Verlag GmbH, Düsseldorf 1981

Printed in Germany

ISBN 3-18-404081-X

Contents

Fundamental principles of the filtration of non-Newtonian liquids

Manfred H. Pahl

Polymer melts and solutions contain foreign particles and other contaminants which interfere to varying degrees during processing and/or when the end product is being used, depending on their size and quantity. In melt spinning for example, such contaminants cause the extruded filaments to tear. In films they cause cloudiness and in cable insulation changes in resistance. Contaminants are introduced into the polymer melt with the raw materials, during processing or when processing regrind.

Contaminants are divided into three groups:

a) Foreign bodies such as metal swarf, sand, pieces of sealing material, fluff.

b) Small pieces of catalyst residue from the polymerising reactor, degraded material which has accumulated, pigment agglomerates.

c) Gel particles of similar chemical composition as the polymer. Different residence times, mixing conditions and temperature differences cause local cross-linkage, especially in the case of nylon and PETP. This results in the formation of gel particles and these are also found in polymer solutions where the polymer has not dissolved completely.

Contaminant particles can be hard and rigid, rubbery or of high viscosity.

There are various methods of determining foreign particles and gels [1 − 3]. Gey [3] compared various methods (table 1) and found that in most of these the amount of sample examined is too small and that only few methods are capable of differentiating between foreign bodies and gels.

The removal of these contaminats with particle sizes ranging from about 5 μm to a few millimeters is achieved by filtration. It is always advisable to clean the raw materials before polymerisation since separation requires the least energy when low viscosity products are involved.

Methods of filtration, filter media

Filtration or filtering is the term applied in chemical engineering practice to the separation of solid particles from a fluid, using a filter element or screen.

1

Table 1. Methods of determining foreign bodies and gels in thermoplastic polymer melts [3].

Type of examination	Method of test	Approx. weight of sample	Determination of foreign bodies	Determination of gels	Suitability[1]) for differentiating between foreign bodies and gels	differentiating between interfering and non-interfering gels	Assessment of degree of dispersion of pigments	Chemical analysis of foreign bodies and gels
Visual counting	microtome section	5 to 20 mg	–	–	–	–	+	–
	film from solution	2 to 3 g	+	(+)	(+)	–	+	–
	Bell telephone test	50 mg	+	–	–	–	+	–
	determination of fish eyes	10 g	+	+	+	+	+	–
Mechanical, photo-electric, conducto-metric counting	determination of small lumps	100 g	+	+	+	+	(+)	–
	conductometric method	10 g	+	+	(–)	+	–	–
	interference measurement	10 g	+	+	–	–	–	–
	optical method	1000 g	+	+	–	–	–	–
Filtration of solutions		15 g	–	+	(+)	–	(+)	–

1) + suitable
(+) suitable under certain conditions
– unsuitable

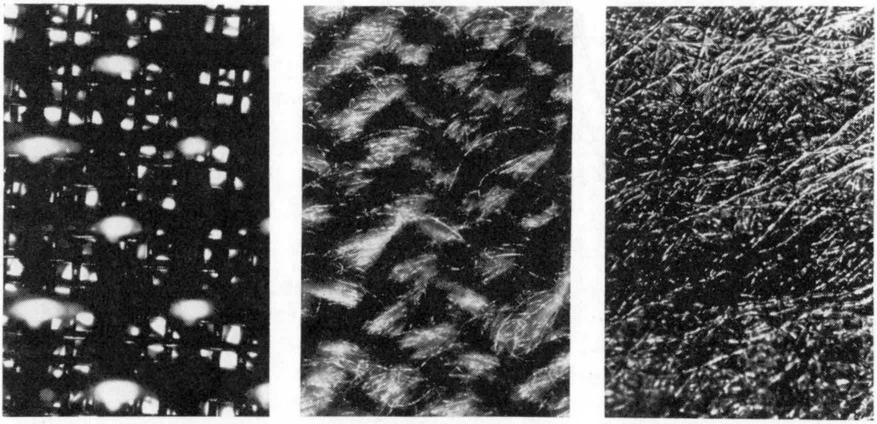

Fig. 1. Some typical filter media (magnification 100 : 1).
a) multi-layer filter cloth, plain weave
b) textile fabric
c) bonded metal fibre mat

Materials used as filter elements include wire gauze, textile fabrics, non-woven mats, skins, membranes, loose material and sintered filters. Three examples are shown in fig. 1. The materials used for these filters include metals, plastics, natural products (cotton), asbestos, glass and ceramics. Metal screens can today be obtained in ten different weave patterns [4 − 6], and they are divided into those that allow light to pass through and those that do not. The pore size of filter elements can be controlled up to a point. In the case of skins, the minimum pore size is about 2 mm, in mats about 1 μm and screens about 5 μm. Filter media do not have a uniform pore size. Fig. 2 shows the sum quantity distribution Q_0 of mesh widths w of woven screens according to DIN 4188. It is evident that even with analytical screens with a mesh width of 50 μm, the actual figure varies between 38 and 66 μm [7].

The separating mechanisms are divided into three groups [8, 9], namely
a) cake filtration (surface filtration)
b) depth filtration (bed filtration)
c) screen filtration (surface filtration).

3

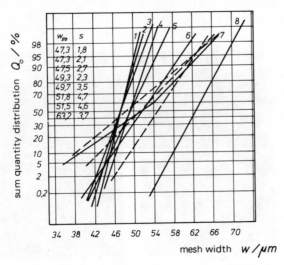

Fig. 2. Comparison of filter cloths according to DIN 4188 having a rated mesh width of 50 μm [7].

w_{50} = mesh width for a sum quantity distribution of 50 %
s = standard deviation

If, for example, one separates suspension polymer from water, the polymer particles will form a so-called cake on the surface of the filter medium, through which the liquid flows (fig. 3a). The cake thickness L_K can be calculated from the amount of solid, if the porosity ϵ is known, using the following equation:

$$c_\alpha \dot{V}_\alpha = c_\omega \dot{V}_\omega + (1 - \epsilon) A \rho_s \frac{dL_K}{dt} \tag{1a}$$

where $\dot{V}_\alpha$ and $\dot{V}_\omega$ are the volume throughputs before and after filtration, A is the cross-section of the empty pipe and

$$c = \frac{m_s}{V_{tot.}} = \frac{\rho_s V_s}{V_{tot.}} = \text{concentration}[1]$$

If one solves equation (1a) with regard to L_K, we obtain

---

1) further symbols are given at the end of this paper

4

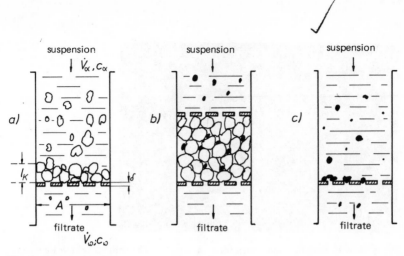

Fig. 3. Filtration techniques.
a) cake filtration
b) depth filtration
c) surface filtration

$$\Delta L_K = \frac{1}{A} \int_{t_1}^{t_2} \frac{c_\alpha \dot{V}_\alpha - c_\omega \dot{V}_\omega}{(1-\epsilon)\rho_s} \, dt \tag{1b}$$

If the volume throughput is kept constant and if the concentrations c and the porosity do not alter during filtration, the following applies, with $\dot{V}_\alpha \approx \dot{V}_\omega = \dot{V}$

$$\Delta L_K = \frac{(c_\alpha - c_\omega)\dot{V}}{(1-\epsilon)\rho_s A} \Delta t \tag{2}$$

In deep filtration (fig. 3b) the particles are separated not on the filter surface but inside the screen pack. In gas purification, the filtration effect is based mainly on adsorption, in polymer melt filtration on physical blockage of the filter pores. Sand bed and metal swarf filters are found, for example, in the production of synthetic fibres, immediately in front of the spinneret. Such filters have been designed to disperse and separate gel particles.

To clean polymer melts in extruders, it is common practice to fit what is known as a screen pack before the melt enters the diehead. A screen pack consists of several filter screens which are mechanically supported by breaker

5

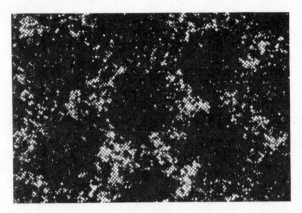

Fig. 4. Heavily contaminated screen from an extruder. The light areas indicate where the screen had been supported by the breaker plate.

plates. If one considers the contaminant particles after filtration, with pressure drops of up to 100 bar, one realises that only one particle layer lies on the screen — or very few layers at most (figs. 3c and 4). The particles, some of which are deformable and are coated with the high viscosity melt, are deposited on the free openings which they block up almost completely. If there is a partial build-up of a cake, there are three possibilities as the pressure increases:

1. the particle bridges remain stable,
2. the particles are deformed,
3. the particles move sideways and block other free screen openings.

Where the separating effect is determined exclusively by the mesh width or pores of the filter medium, one speaks of surface filtration. It should be noted that the screen effect is greatly influenced by the particle shape (fig. 5).

Fitting a screen pack, consisting of breaker plate and several screens, between the screw tip and the die orifice of older extruder models aims not only at filtration but also serves to improve screw performance [10].

In certain filtration processes it is impossible to differentiate between the above three mechanisms. The process frequently starts with surface filtration, then a cake builds up within which depth filtration occurs. To improve the separating efficiency of the filter cake, filtration aids such as kieselguhr or sawdust are used when filtering low viscosity media.

6

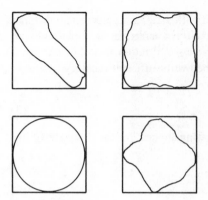

Fig. 5. Differently shaped particles with the same mesh width.

In order to be better able to understand the flow processes in the filter, let us first consider the flow inside a capillary.

Tubular flow of non-Newtonian liquids

Most polymer melts exhibit Newtonian, as well as non-Newtonian and visco-elastic behaviour at shear rates of $\dot{\gamma} \geqslant 0.1 \ s^{-1}$ (fig. 6). One must therefore find out in which range polymer melt filtration is carried out.

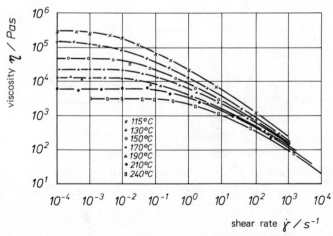

Fig. 6. Viscosity function of the melt of a branched polyethylene at different temperatures (ρ_{20} = 0.92 kg/dm^3, melt flow index = 1.3) [11].

7

As an example, let us take an extruder with a 120 mm screw and a through-put of 500 dm³/h [12]. The filter element is a screen fabric in plain weave, with a mesh width of 50 μm and an effective filtration area of 0.7 A (fig. 7). Assuming that the melt can be described with sufficient accuracy by the Ostwald-de Waele equation [13]

$$\dot{\gamma} = \phi\, \tau^n \tag{3}$$

and that the flow index ≈ 2, the following applies: for the flow rate $\bar{v}_L$ in an empty pipe:

$$\bar{v}_L = \frac{4\,\dot{V}}{\pi\, D^2} = 1{,}2 \text{ cm/s} \tag{4}$$

for the wall shear rate $\dot{\gamma}_L$ in an empty pipe [13]

$$\dot{\gamma}_L = \frac{n+3}{\pi}\, \frac{8\,\dot{V}_{tot.}}{D^3} \tag{5}$$

$$\dot{\gamma}_L = 1 \text{ s}^{-1}$$

for the flow rate $\bar{v}_s$ in the screen

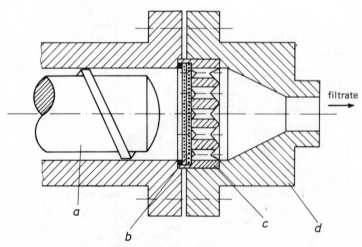

Fig. 7. Arrangement of a screen pack in an extruder.
a) screw,   b) screens,   c) breaker plate,   d) die

$$\bar{v}_s = \frac{\bar{v}_L \, A}{A_H} = 1{,}7 \text{ cm/s}$$ (6)

for the wall shear rate $\dot{\gamma}_s$ in the screen

$$\dot{\gamma}_s \approx \frac{2(n+3)\,\bar{v}_s}{w} = 3{,}4 \times 10^3 \text{ s}^{-1}$$ (5a)

It is evident from fig. 6 that filtration takes place in the non-Newtonian range and that the viscosity in the filter is reduced by a factor of 10/100.

To understand the flow processes in the filter let us first consider a liquid flowing through a capillary. As fig. 8 shows, the liquid accelerates along the distance AC from a speed of $\bar{v}_A$ to the almost plug flow speed $\bar{v}_C$. According to Bernoulli, the kinetic energy can be expressed as a pressure decrease [14]

$$\Delta p \Big/ {}^C_A = \frac{\rho_f}{2} \, (\bar{v}_C^2 - \bar{v}_A^2)$$ (7)

In the inlet zone, the final flow profile is formed, the layers near the walls being slowed down and those nearer the centre being speeded up. For this to occur, a pressure decrease

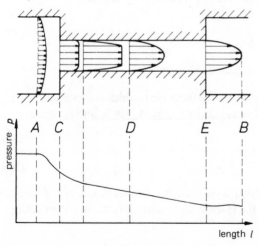

Fig. 8. Change in flow profile and pressure drop along a capillary [14].

9

$$\Delta p \Big/ {\textstyle\frac{D}{C}} = \rho_f \bar{v}_C^2/2 \tag{8}$$

is necessary[2]).

Since a rectangular liquid stream produces greater friction than one with a parabolic profile, the increased pressure drop along distance CD is determined by means of the so-called Couette correction which consists of adding an imaginary distance L_c to the length L of the capillary.

Applying Ostwald-de Waele's equation (3), the frictional pressure drop inside the pipe, with laminar, isothermal, stationary flow, can be expressed by the following equation [13]

$$\Delta p = \frac{4\,L}{D} \left(\frac{8(n+3)\,\dot{V}}{\pi\,\phi\,D^3} \right)^{1/n} \tag{9a}$$

or

$$\Delta p = \frac{4\,L}{D} \left(\frac{2(n+3)\,\bar{v}}{\phi\,D} \right)^{1/n} \tag{9b}$$

When visco-elastic melts flow through channels, there is an additional elastic deformation analogous to fig. 9 Most of the deformation is maintained inside the capillary and relaxes only on leaving it. This Bagley effect can be taken into account in equation (9) by an imaginary distance

$$L^* = \left(\frac{L}{D} + B \right) D \tag{10}$$

the Bagley factor for thermoplastics being $\approx 2.5 - 3$.

The friction inside the capillaries produces heat, which is important when calculating the viscosity. For an adiabatic process the following applies:

$$\dot{E} = \Delta p \dot{V} = \rho_f\,\dot{V}\,c\,\Delta T \tag{11a}$$

$$\Delta T = \Delta p/(\rho_f\,c) \tag{11b}$$

If one now applies these conditions to surface filtration, one can assume for high viscosity media that the Hagenbach-Couette effects are not so noticeable because

---

2) In rheology, these effects are determined by the Hagenbach correction.

10

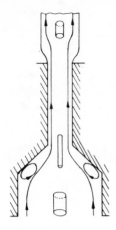

Fig. 9. Deformation of a cylindrical fluid element when flowing through a nozzle [13].

— the speeds are slow,
— the effective screen area is usually of the same size as the flow channel,
— the inlets are well rounded, due to the shape of the wires.

A visco-elastic effect is to be expected in the case of screens, although here, too, the openings are round and the screen meshes should in fact be regarded as three-dimensional. In thicker felts and in filter cakes other deformation rates are always encountered.

Filter equations

Let us now consider a filter with filter cake and filter element placed in a channel with the cross-sectional area A. If one imagines the filter cake to be a system of pores with coiled capillaries, equation (9b) can be transformed, using the symbols from fig. 10, into the following equation:

$$\Delta p = \frac{k\, l_p}{d_p} \left(\frac{\bar{v}_p}{d_p}\right)^{\frac{1}{n}} \tag{12}$$

with

$$k = 4 \left[\frac{2(n+3)}{\phi}\right]^{1/n}$$

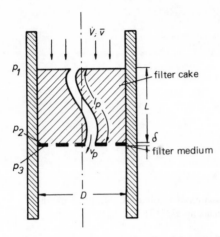

Fig. 10. Nomenclature used to formulate the filter equation.

Since the pore length l_p is not known, the speed $\bar{v}_p$ of the fluid inside the pores is replaced by an imaginary speed v where

$$v = \frac{L}{t}; \quad \bar{v}_p = \frac{l_p}{t}$$

and

$$v = \frac{L}{l_p} \bar{v}_p \tag{13}$$

The speed v inside the pore system can also be converted into a speed $\bar{v}$ related to the cross-section of the empty tube $A = \pi D^2/4$. From the continuity law it follows that

$$A\bar{v} = A_H v \tag{14}$$

For random homogeneous packings, the ratio of free cross-sectional area A_H to the total area A corresponds to the volume porosity ϵ

$$\frac{A_H}{A} = \frac{V_H}{V} = \epsilon \tag{15}$$

12

Using equations (14) and (15), equation (13) becomes

$$v_p = \frac{l_p}{L} \frac{\bar{v}}{\epsilon} \tag{16}$$

If one replaces the pore diameter d_p by the hydraulic diameter

$$d_h = \frac{4\,A_H\,L}{U\,L} = \frac{4 \times \text{pore volume}}{\text{surface area of solid}}$$

then

$$d_h = \frac{4\,\dfrac{\text{pore volume}}{\text{total volume}}}{\dfrac{\text{solid surface area}}{\text{solid volume}}\,\dfrac{\text{solid volume}}{\text{total volume}}}$$

$$d_h = \frac{4}{S_v} \frac{\epsilon}{(1-\epsilon)} \tag{17a}$$

If one then introduces the particle diameter x for the volume-related surface area S_v, we get

$$S_v = \frac{6}{x} \tag{18}$$

$$d_h = \frac{2}{3} \frac{\epsilon}{(1-\epsilon)\,d_p} \; x \tag{17b}$$

From equations (12), (16) and (17b) it follows that

$$\Delta p = k \left(\frac{3}{2}\right)^{1+\frac{1}{n}} \left(\frac{l_p}{L}\right)^{1+\frac{1}{n}} \frac{(1-\epsilon)}{\epsilon^{1+2/n}}^{1+\frac{1}{n}} \; x \; \bar{v}^{1+\frac{1}{n}} \cdot L^{\frac{1}{n}} \tag{19a}$$

For Newtonian liquids with $n = 1$, equation (19a) changes into the Kozeny-Carman equation [15]

$$\Delta p = 72 \left(\frac{l_p}{L}\right)^2 \eta \frac{(1-\epsilon)^2}{\epsilon^3} \; x^2 \bar{v} L \tag{20}$$

13

from which one obtains the coil factor

$$\left(\frac{l_p}{L}\right)^2 \approx 2.5$$

for isometric particles.

Tests have shown that equation (20), derived from the so-called channel model, has only limited validity [14, 15].

In contrast to the Kozeny-Carman relationship, the influence of packing parameters such as porosity and particle diameter on pressure decrease in equation (19a) is dependent upon the flow index n of the medium through which the liquid passes. The comparison further shows that changes in the packing structure and the volume throughput have less effect on non-Newtonian liquids than on Newtonian ones.

If a melt with an approximately constant flow index passes through a filter cake, equation (19a) can be simplified into

$$\Delta p = \frac{L}{B_1} \, \bar{v}^{\,1/n} \tag{19b}$$

The filter cake thickness L changes during filtration and is, for the moment, unknown. If one draws up the solids balance

filter cake mass = solid mass in filtrate

$$LA(1 - \epsilon)\, \rho_s = (V + AL\epsilon)\rho_f y \tag{21a}$$

with

$$y = M_s/M_f$$

then one can put

$$L = \frac{\rho_f \, y}{(1 - \epsilon)\rho_s - \epsilon\rho_f \, y} \, \frac{V}{A} = k_1 \, \frac{V}{A} \tag{21b}$$

k_1 gives us the ratio of filter cake volume to filtrate volume. Since, furthermore,

$$\bar{v} = \frac{1}{A} \, \frac{dV}{dt} \tag{22}$$

14

one can obtain the pressure drop in the filter cake from equations (19b), (21b) and (22) from

$$\Delta p_K = \frac{k_1}{B_1} \frac{V}{A^{1-1/n}} \left(\frac{dV}{dt}\right)^{1/n}$$ (23)

Equation (19a) can serve directly to describe the filter medium if this can be regarded as a randomly homogeneous aggregate such as packed sand, felt or frit.

With filter screens one often follows another line of approach. The simplest way [17, 18] is to put, in equation (9b)

twice the wire diameter as the length of flow:

$$L = 2\, d_s$$ (24a)

the mesh width as the hydraulic diameter:

$$D = d_h = w$$ (24b)

and the expression

$$v_s = \frac{A}{A_H}\, \bar{v} = \left(\frac{d_s + w}{d_s}\right)^2 \bar{v}$$ (24c)

as the flow rate in the meshes. Then we obtain

$$\Delta p_F = \frac{8\, d_s}{w} \left[\frac{2(n+3)\, \bar{v}}{\phi\, w} \left(\frac{d_s + w}{w}\right)^2\right]^{1/n}$$ (25a)

If one introduces the volume throughput $\dot{V}$ in place of the speed $\bar{v}$ in the empty cross-section A, then equation (25a) becomes

$$\Delta p_s = \frac{8\, d_s}{w^{1+1/n}} \left[\frac{2(n+3)\, (d_s + w)^2}{\phi\, w^2}\right]^{1/n} \left(\frac{\dot{V}}{A}\right)^{1/n}$$ (25b)

If one looks more closely at the meshes of a screen (fig. 11), the geometry can be determined more accurately through other integral parameters. Blass [19] has calculated the porosity ϵ and the ratio φ of screen surface area to total volume for different filter cloths and makes

the hydraulic diameter

$$d_h = \sqrt{\epsilon/z}$$ (26a)

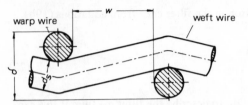

Fig. 11. Cross-section through the mesh of a filter medium.

the speed in the filter cloth

$$\bar{v}_s = \bar{v}/\epsilon \qquad (26b)$$

the ratio of packing length L to hydraulic diameter d_h

$$L/d_h = \delta\,\varphi/\epsilon \qquad (26c)$$

and finds the following for the laminar flow of Newtonian liquids

$$\Delta p = \frac{c_B\,\delta\,\varphi\,\sqrt{z}\,\eta}{\epsilon^{2,5}}\,\bar{v} \qquad (26d)$$

where the parameter is $33 < c_B < 34$, depending on the filter cloth.

If one transfers these figures to non-Newtonian media and puts $c_B = 32$, then it follows from equation (9b) that

$$\Delta p_s = \frac{4\,\delta\,\varphi}{\epsilon}\left[\frac{2(n+3)\,\bar{v}}{\phi\,\sqrt{\epsilon/z}\,\epsilon}\right]^{1/n} \qquad (27)$$

Armour and Cannon [20] give the following relationship for Newtonian liquids

$$\Delta p_s = c_A\,\eta\,\delta\,\bar{v}\,\varphi^2/\epsilon^2 \qquad (28)$$

Another method of determining the pressure drop is based not on the throughflow model but on the flow around cylinders [15, 20].

In the case of pure surface filtration and assuming that the boundary layer between filter cake and filter medium does not cause increased pressure drop, the total pressure decrease of filter cake and filter medium is given by

$$\Delta p_{tot.} = \Delta p_K + \Delta p_F \qquad (29)$$

16

If one inserts equations (23) and (25b) in equation (29) the following applies for n = const.

$$\frac{dV}{dt} = \left(\frac{\Delta p}{\dfrac{k_1}{B_1} \dfrac{V}{A^{1+1/n}} + \dfrac{k_2}{A^{1/n}}} \right)^n \tag{30}$$

Equation (30) is referred to as a filter equation. It can be integrated if $\Delta p(\dot{V})$ is known. In extruders, the volume throughput decreases with increasing back pressure. If one assumes, in first approximation, a constant volume throughput, then we get

$$\Delta p = \left(\frac{k_1}{B_1} \frac{\dot{V}t}{A^{1+1/n}} + \frac{k_2}{A^{1/n}} \right) \dot{V}^{1/n} \tag{31}$$

In systems with piston pumps, Δp = constant. In this case, equation (30) is transformed into

$$\Delta p^n t = \frac{B_1 A^{1+1/n}}{k_1 (n+1)} \left[\left(\frac{k_1}{B_1} \frac{V}{A^{1+1/n}} + \frac{k_2}{A^{1/n}} \right)^{n+1} - \left(\frac{k_2}{A^{1/n}} \right)^{n+1} \right] \tag{32a}$$

If one further condenses the paramters k_1, k_2, B_1 and A the following applies:

$$\Delta p = [(a V + b)^{1+1/n} - b^{1+1/n}]/t^{1/n} \tag{32b}$$

In interpreting equation (32b) it should be noted that the parameters a and b themselves depend upon the flow index n and that the filter cake has been assumed to be incompressible.

The difficulty in calculating a filtration process in advance is usually that the size and shape of the separated particles and the porosity of the filter cake in relation to pressure [21] are not known. This is why experiments are always carried out in the case of unknown substances, even Newtonian liquids.

The filtration of polymer melts in filter screens can also be interpreted if one introduces, in equation (25b), a degree of contamination $(A_H - A_{sch})/A_H$ and the Bagley correction, similar to equation (10). If one further replaces the fluiditiy ϕ

17

$$\phi = \frac{1}{\eta^n \, \dot{\gamma}^{n-1}} \tag{33a}$$

then the following applies

$$\Delta p = \frac{4 \left(\dfrac{2\,ds}{w} + \alpha B\right) w}{w^{1+1/n}} \left[2(n+3) \left(\frac{d_s + w}{w^2}\right)^2\right]^{1/n} \eta \, \dot{\gamma}^{1-1/n}$$

$$x \left(\frac{\dot{V}}{A}\right)^{1/n} \left(\frac{A_H}{A_H - A_{sch}}\right)^{1/n} \tag{33}$$

the correction factor, according to [18] being ≈ 0.3.

From equation (33) one can see that the following pressure decreases occur for a melt with a flow index of 2 under the circumstances listed:

doubling of mesh width	$\Delta p / \Delta p_0$	0.3
doubling of volume throughput	$\Delta p / \Delta p_0$	1.4
doubling of free screen area	$\Delta p / \Delta p_0$	0.7
dirt blocks up half the screens	$\Delta p / \Delta p_0$	1.4
dirt blocks up 3/4 of the screens	$\Delta p / \Delta p_0$	2

From equation (1a) we obtain the dirty screen area as

$$A_{sch} \sim c\dot{V}t \tag{34}$$

so that, from equation (33) it follows that

$$\Delta p \sim [1/(1 - \beta\dot{V}t)]^{1/n} \tag{35}$$

Experimental determination of filter performance and degree of separation

In the case of low viscosity solutions, filter performance is often determined using a manual suction filter [8]. For high viscosity media, the determination is often carried out direct on the production unit to ensure that the operating parameters are the same. Brignac and Marks [2] have described a test set-up with an extruder. They also give details of the accuracy with which pressures, temperatures, volume throughputs and times can be determined. Brabender, Duisburg, offers a filtration apparatus shown in fig. 12, which can also be used to determine viscosity.

18

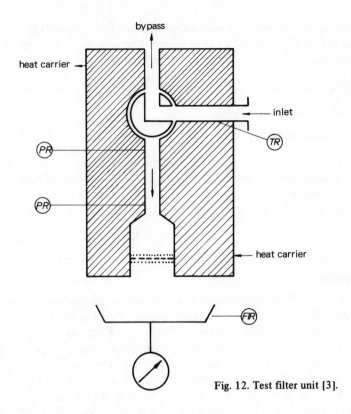

Fig. 12. Test filter unit [3].

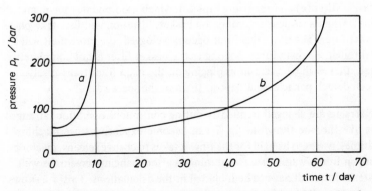

Fig. 13. Melt pressure in front of the filter as a function of time (Material: nylon 66) [17].

Fig. 13 shows an experimental pressure profile as a function of time [17]. Here one can see the effectiveness of an increased filter area. It should also be pointed out that, in many processes, a filter will last only a few hours.

The separation efficiency is often charaterised by the degree of separation

$$\eta_T = \frac{\text{amount of separated solids}}{\text{amount of solids introduced}}$$

Easily separated, large particles greatly increase the degree of separation, whereas the small, difficult to separate particles are hardly included in this quantity. It is therefore expedient to introduce the size of the separated particles or the fractional degree of separation as characteristic quantity [22].

Design principles

The most widely used filter arrangement in an extruder consists of a set of several screens and a breaker plate to support them, as shown in fig. 7. This design is meaningful only if filtration times are long or the process is often interrupted. The filter will last longer if the filter area is increased. Large filters should be accomodated in a small housing so as to keep residence times to a minimum. This is possible, for example, by incorporating one or more candle filters, as shown in fig. 14 [23, 24, 25]. Schmauder, Kaufbeuren, offers a screen basket in which the main filter is self-cleaning. This unit (fig. 15) consists of a sleeve (a) into which is inserted the basket (b) with the basket filter (c) and the rising pipe (e), which accomodates the main filter (f). When a suspension enters the basket, filtration will first take place in basket filter. The more this filter becomes clogged, the more melt will flow through the main filter. As long as the basket filter is not completely clogged, there will be a stream impinging on the main filter transversely. This can detach particles and deposit them in the space (d).

If the screens are changed frequently during continuous operation, arrangements like the one shown in fig. 7 can become expensive since machine downtimes, wages to be paid for the time it takes to change screens, machine running-in times, wages paid for running in after changing screens, as well as material losses all have to be included in the calculations. Table 2 shows such a cost breakdown for the use of screens in the production of thermoplastic film and blow mouldings [26].

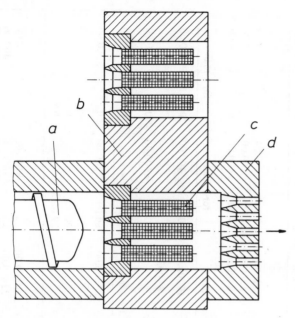

Fig. 14. Screen changer with candle filters [24].

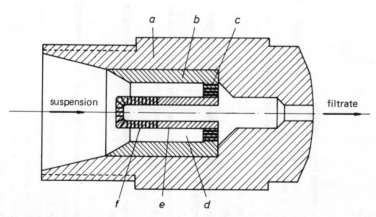

Fig. 15. Filter basket for screening foreign particles.

a) sleeve   d) space for foreign particles
b) basket   e) rising pipe
c) basket screen   f) main filter

21

Table 2. Cost breakdown for the use of screen changers in the production of films, blow mouldings, profiles etc. from thermoplastic materials [26].

Assumed basic figures (averaged actual figures):

Machine costs	DM 80.00/h	
Labour costs	DM 20.00/h	
Screen change cycle	one every 24 h	

Operating period (3 shifts)	24 h/day
No. of screen changes p.a. (240 working days)	240
Working hours p.a.	4,880 h/p.a.

	I Built-in breaker plate with screen pack		II D-SWE screen changer discontinuous		III K-SWE screen changer continuous	
	2,00 h*		0,088 h		0,088 h	
Screen changing time, complete	h	DM	h	DM	h	DM
*) with dismantling and assembly of downstream equipment						
A) Machine downtime during screen chaning						
per day	2	160.00	0,088	7.04	0	0.00
per month	40	3200.00	1,75	140.00	0	0.00
per year	480	38400.00	20,00	1600.00	0	0.00
B) Labour costs for operating period during screen changing	for 2 men		for 1 man		for 1 man	
	960	19200.00	20,00	400.00	20	400.00
C) Machine running-in period after changing screens (20 min per day, 400 min per month)						
per year	80	6400.00	80,00	6400.00	0	0.00
D) Labour costs for running-in period after changing screens	for 2 men		for 2 men		for 1 man	
per year	80	3200.00	80,00	3200.00	0	0.00
E) Annual loss of production due to screen changing, in hours for 4,880 working hours in %	560	11,5 %	100	2,05 %	0	0 %
Summary of annual costs						
1. Machine costs (A + C)		44800.00		8000.00		0.00
2. Labour costs (B + D)		22400.00		3600.00		400.00
Total cost DM		67200.00		11600.00		400.00

22

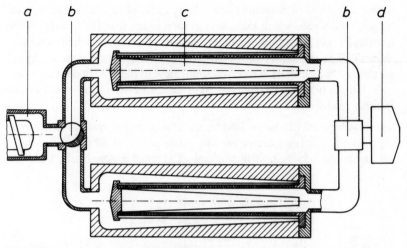

Fig. 16. Screen changer with candle filters [23].
a) screw
b) change-over element
c) candle filter
d) die

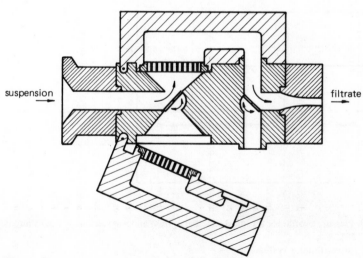

Fig. 17. Screen changer with flat screen [27].

23

A simple method of reducing screen changing times consists of incorporating a second screen which takes over as soon as the first one is dirty. Whilst one screen is in operation, the other one can be cleaned. Such systems are shown in figs. 16 and 17. Both have the disadvantage that there are bypasses through which there is not a constant flow of melt. With delicate materials, there is likely to be degradation or similar deterioration of the material in these dead spots.

This disadvantage can be avoided by so-called slide bar systems as shown in figs. 14 and 18. Tey work rather like a slide projector. Slide bar systems are differentiated into those with mechanical, thermal and hydraulic seals.

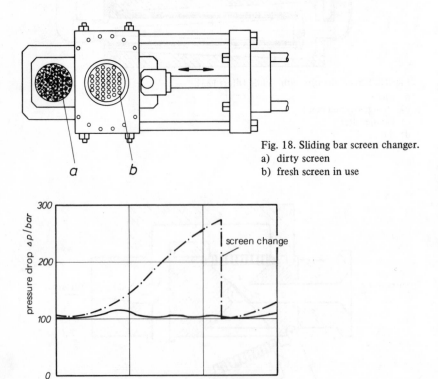

Fig. 18. Sliding bar screen changer.
a) dirty screen
b) fresh screen in use

Fig. 19. Pressure profile for a typical slide bar system and a system with a continuous screen [28].

−.−.− discontinuous system

―――― continuous system

24

The above described, discontinuous screen changers all have the disadvantage that there is a considerable drop in pressure before the screen is changed. Fig. 19 shows a typical pressure profile compared with a system employing a continuous screen. A fully automatic screen changer is shown in fig. 20. A cassette (a) delivers a continuous strip of filter material (b) which passes through the flow channel (i). The dirty screen passes through a water cooled flange (g) which causes the melt to solidify [29]. Today, there are about 20 kinds of screen changers, whose distinguishing features are described in [29].

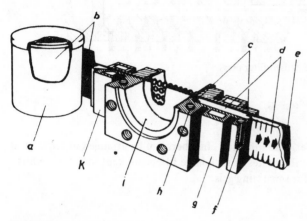

Fig. 20. Diagram of a continuous, fully automatic screen changer [29].
a) screen cassette
b) strip of filter material
c) polymer melt
d) solidified polymer melt with embedded screen
e) start of screen strip
f) cartridge heater
g) water cooled outlet flange for the screen strip
h) adapter
i) flow channel
k) water cooled inlet flange for the screen strip

Besides the above described filters for extruders, chemical plants use large area candle and plate filters, as well as compartmentalised filter presses (fig. 21) consisting of several grooved filter plates (a) over which filter cloths (b) are clamped. The filter plates are hydraulically compressed by means of the end pieces (c). The melt to be cleaned enters the filtration chambers and thence passes through the filter cloth and the grooved filter

25

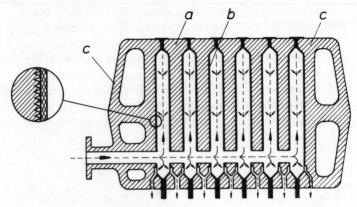

Fig. 21. Compartmentalised filter press.
a) grooved filter plates
b) filter cloth
c) end pieces

plates to the outlet. The filtration chambers can be arranged in series or in parallel. Since the flow rates in such large filters are kept low, these units can also be used for separating gels.

Symbols

A	cross-section of empty channel
A_H	free cross-section in screen
A_{sch}	dirty area of screen
a, b	parameters in equation (32b)
B	Bagley correction according to equation (10)
B_1	permeability factor according to equation (19b)
C_A, C_B	coefficients
c	mass concentration according to equation (1a)
c	specific heat in equation (11b)
D	pipe diameter
d_h	hydraulic diameter
d_p	pore diameter
d_s	wire diameter of screen gauze
$\dot{E}$	efficiency
k	parameter in equation (12)
k_1	filter cake volume/filtrate volume

k_2	parameter from equation (25c)
L	length
L_K	thickness of filter cake
l_p	pore length
M_s	solid mass
M_f	filtrate mass
n	flow index in equation (3)
Δp	pressure drop
Δp_K	pressure drop in filter cake
Δp_F	pressure drop in filter medium
Δp_s	pressure drop in filter cloth
S_v	volume-related solid surface
T	temperature
t	time
U	circumference
V	volume
V_H	pore volume
$\dot{V}$	volume throughput
$\dot{V}_\alpha$	suspension volume throughput
$\dot{V}_\omega$	filtrate volume throughput
v	velocity
$\bar{v}, \bar{v}_L$	mean velocity related to cross-section of empty pipe
$\bar{v}_S$	mean velocity in screen or filter
$\bar{v}_p$	velocity in the pores
w	mesh width
x	particle diameter
y	mass ratio
z	number of meshes per unit area
α, β	parameters
$\dot{\gamma}$	shear rate
δ	filter medium thickness
ϵ	porosity
η	degree of separation
ρ_f	fluid density
ρ_s	solid density
τ	shear stress
ϕ	fluidity
φ	filter cloth surface/total volume

Bibliography

[1] *Menges, G.* a. *V. Giegerich:* Berichte zum 6. Kunststofftechnischen Kolloquium des IKV in Aachen, 1972, pp. 88/92.

[2] *Brognac, E. P.* a. *W. J. Marks:* Filtration and Separation (1977) July/Aug., pp. 362/366.

[3] *Gey, W.:* Kunststoffe 66 (1976) 6, pp. 329/333.

[4] N. N.: Minimesh, Metall-Drahtgewebe, Leaflet published by Haver a. Boecker, Oelde, 1979.

[5] *Nickolaus, N.:* Filtration and Separation (1975) March/April, pp. 155/163.

[6] *Schönbauer, G.:* In this book.

[7] *Leschonski, K.:* Getreide und Mehl 10 (1960) 12, pp. 140/174.

[8] *Alt, Chr.:* Ullmann's Enzyklopädie, Verlag Chemie, Weinheim, 1973.

[9] *Coulson, J. M.* a. *J. M. Richardson:* Chemical Engineering, Bd. 2, Pergamon Press, 1978.

[10] *Schenkel, G.:* Kunststoff-Extrudertechnik, Hanser-Verlag, München, 1963.

[11] *Meissner, J.:* Praktische Rheologie der Kunststoffe, VDI-Verlag, Düsseldorf, 1978.

[12] *Predöhl, W.:* Technologie extrudierter Kunststoffolien, VDI-Verlag, Düsseldorf, 1979.

[13] *Pahl, M. H.:* Praktische Rheologie der Kunststoffe, VDI-Verlag, Düsseldorf, 1978.

[14] *Muschelknautz, E.* a. *M. Heckenbach:* Messen, Steuern und Regeln in der chemischen Technik. Springer-Verlag, Berlin, 1980.

[15] *Pahl, M. H.:* Dissertation, Karlsruhe, 1975.

[16] *Brauer, H.:* Grundlagen der Ein- und Mehrphasenströmung, Verlag Sauerländer, Aarau, 1971.

[17] *Hensen, F.* a. *H. Siemetzki:* Kunststoffe 70 (1980) 11, pp. 753/758.

[18] *Brauer, W., G. Ehrmann* a. *W. Schneider:* In this book.

[19] *Blass, E.:* Chemie-Ing.-Techn. 36 (1964) 7, pp. 747/758.

[20] *Armour, J. C.* a. *J. N. Cannon:* AIChE-Journal 14 (1968) 3, pp. 415/420.

[21] *Tiller, F. M.:* Filtration and Separation 4 (1975) pp. 389/94.

[22] *Leschonski, K.:* Ullmann's Encyklopädie der chemischen Technik, Verlag Chemie, Weinheim, 1973.

[23] *Hensen, F.* a. *E. Gathmann:* Kunststoffe 64 (1974) 7, pp. 343/349.

[24] AS 2119545.

[25] N. N.: Leaflet published by Fuji Filter, Tokio.

[26] *Kreyenborg, U.:* Kunststofftechnik 13 (1974) 5, pp. 92/94.

[27] *Voight, B. R.:* Modern Plastics (1966) August, pp. 125/127.

[28] N. N.: Leaflet published by Berlyn, Worcester, 1976.

[29] *Escales, E.:* Kunststoffe 69 (1978) 11, pp. 751/752.

[30] *Collins, S. H.:* Plastics Maschinery and equipment 9 (1980) 12, pp. 751/752.

Lay-out and design of breaker plates

Ullrich Masberg

To achieve high quality in the manufacture and processing of thermoplastics, it is not only important to have a homogeneous melt and smooth passage of the melt through the die, among other things — but it is also extremely important to have an absolutely clean melt, free from solid contanimants. This applies particularly to the production of stretched film, pipes or filaments.

The necessary melt homogeneity is produced by the extruder whereas melt purity is achieved by a suitable filtration system. Gel particles, dust etc. are separated from the melt by using very fine-mesh filter elements.

The construction and method of operation of filtration systems have been described for example in [1] and [2], and will be further discussed in the papers presented at this conference. The most widely used basic form consists of a multi-layer screen pack made up of screens with different fineness, and a breaker plate.

In the filtration of polymer melts, the function of the breaker plate is to mechanically support to screen pack against the difference in pressure in the melt stream. Correctly designed, it can, in conjunction with the screens, achieve further homogenisation of the melt.

The supporting function of the breaker plate should be such that the screens do not rupture near the holes in the breaker plate and that the screens are adequately supported even when the pressure increases due to the screens becoming clogged. Proper functioning of the breaker plate thus depends on the type of screen, flow conditions and on the actual breaker plate design.

It should be noted that the method of rheological and mechanical design of the breaker plate, described below, can also be used for pelletiser dies. This applies particularly to the rheological design.

Rheological calculation principles

In order to be able to design the various components of a filtration system it is necessary to determine the maximum pressure loss likely to occur. This is dependent on geometric conditions, the required maximum throughput and the melt viscosity.

Description of the viscosity behaviour takes into account its change as a function of shear rate and temperature T:

$$\eta = f(\dot{\gamma}, T) \tag{1}$$

The dependence of viscosity on pressure and time will not be taken into account here, since it is unimportant for our particular problem.

Mathematical theorems for describing viscosity behaviour

To calculate pressure loss, it is necessary to know the viscosity behaviour during operation and to introduce this into our calculations.

Many different mathematical theorems are now used to describe the viscosity behaviour. They vary in complexity and fairly accurately describe the actual behaviour.

The most widely used formulations are

1. Ostwald – de Waele's exponential theorem
2. Münstedt's polynomial theorem
3. Vinogradow's viscosity theorem
4. Carreau's viscosity theorem.

The last named theorem will be used in a book, soon to be published by the VDMA, for characterising the viscosity behaviour of a large number of thermoplastics. We shall not concern ourselves with the mathematical representation and the necessary constants for the various viscosity theorems, this having been dealt with by numerous authors [3, 5, 6, 15, 16].

Principle of representative viscosity

It is usually a problem to employ the above mathematical theorems to calculate pressure losses and other quantities since these often lead to unwieldy mathematical equations.

This problem is avoided by the principle of representative viscosity, which assumes that within a melt flow-way there is a point where the shear rates for a Newtonian and a non-Newtonian substance are identical if one assumes the same volume throughput for both cases. This idea is explained in fig. 1.

30

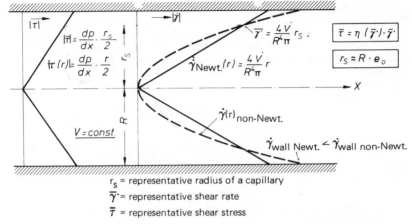

$$|\bar{\tau}| = \frac{dp}{dx} \cdot \frac{r_s}{2}$$

$$|\tau(r)| = \frac{dp}{dx} \cdot \frac{r}{2}$$

$$\dot{\bar{\gamma}} = \frac{4V}{R^4\pi} r_s$$

$$\dot{\gamma}_{Newt.}(r) = \frac{4V}{R^4\pi} r$$

$$\bar{\tau} = \eta\,(\dot{\bar{\gamma}})\cdot\dot{\bar{\gamma}}$$

$$r_s \approx R \cdot e_0$$

$V = const$

$\dot{\gamma}(r)_{non-Newt.}$

$\dot{\gamma}_{wall\ Newt.} < \dot{\gamma}_{wall\ non-Newt.}$

r_s = representative radius of a capillary
$\dot{\bar{\gamma}}$ = representative shear rate
$\bar{\tau}$ = representative shear stress

Fig. 1. Determination of the "representative viscosity" from the "representative" shear rate and the "representative" shear stress in a round-section flow channel.

If one determines the shear stress and the shear rate at this point, one obtains the true viscosity for the "representative" shear rate at that point. The position of the point of intersection can be regarded as constant for many polymers.

Table 1 shows the relationships necessary for determining shear rate for the basic geometries of circle, annular slit and rectangular slit.

The following procedure is adopted:

1. Determination of representative shear rate in the melt flow-way section.

2. Determination of representative viscosity at the calculated representative shear rate from
   a) flow or viscosity curves,
   b) the viscosity theorems from section 3.1.

3. Putting the representative viscosity into relationships derived for Newtonian substances. Determination of pressure loss.

A simple example will also clarify the procedure:

Calculation of the pressure loss in a circular pipe, 15 cm long and a diameter of 1.69 cm at a volume throughput $\dot{V}$ of 18.37 cm³/s (which is equivalent to a mass throughput $\dot{m}$ of 200 kg/h HDPE at a temperature of 190 °C). This

31

Table 1. Calculation of representative shear rate.

Geometry	non-Newtonian viscosity: representative figures
circular opening (pipe)	$\bar{\dot{\gamma}} = \dfrac{4\,\dot{V}}{\pi\,R^3}\,e_0 \qquad\qquad \bar{e}_0 = 0.815$
Annular slit	$\bar{\dot{\gamma}} = \dfrac{\dot{V}}{(R_a^2 - R_i^2)\,R} = \pi\,\dfrac{\bar{v}}{R}$ $\bar{R} = R_a\left(1 + k^2 + \dfrac{1-k^2}{\ln k}\right)^{0,5}$ $k = \dfrac{R_i}{R_a}$
Rectangular slit	$\bar{\dot{\gamma}} = \dfrac{6\,\dot{V}}{B\,H^2}\,e_\square \qquad\qquad \bar{e}_\square = 0.772$ The $e_{0,\square}$ figures apply to flow exponents $2 \leqslant m \geqslant 4$ as mean values

calculation for the isothermal case ($a_T = 1$) is performed with the help of two viscosity theorems:

1. Ostwald – de Waele's exponential theorem (No. 1)

$$\eta_1 = K_{oT} \times \dot{\gamma}^m$$
$$K_{oT} = 7.8 \times 10^4 \text{ Pa} \times s^{0.4}; m = 0.6$$

2. Münstedt's polynomial theorem (No. 2)

$$\log \eta_2 = \sum_{n=0}^{4} K_n\,(\log(\dot{\gamma}))^n$$

$K_0 = 5.6812 \qquad K_1 = 0.72476 \qquad K_2 = 0.207517 \qquad K_3 = 0.075264$
$K_4 = 9.0364 \times 10^{-3}$

First of all, the representative shear rate $\bar{\dot{\gamma}}$ is calculated using the procedure explained above (see table 1):

$$\bar{\gamma} = \frac{4\,\dot{V}}{\pi\,R^3} \times e_0 = \frac{4 \times 18.37 \; cm^3/s}{\pi \left(\dfrac{1.69}{2}\right)^3 \; cm^3} \times 0.815$$

$$\bar{\gamma} = 31.6 \; s^{-1}$$

In a second step, the representative shear rate $\bar{\gamma}$ is put into the viscosity theorems and the representative viscosity $\bar{\eta}$ calculated:

1. Ostwald – de Waele's theorem

   $\bar{\eta}_1 = 9.82 \times 10^3 \; Pa \cdot s$

2. Münstedt's theorem

   $\bar{\eta}_2 = 9.78 \times 10^3 \; Pa \cdot s$

In a third step, the pressure loss is determined, using the calculated representative viscosities:

$$\Delta p = \frac{8\,\bar{\eta}_{1.2}\,\dot{V}}{\pi\,R^4}\,L$$

with the result

$\Delta p_1 = 134.6 \; bar$ $\qquad$ $\Delta p_2 = 134.1 \; bar$

In the remarks that follow, this method is preferred.

Calculation of pressure losses when using breaker plates

Breaker plates are designed with reference to the total pressure loss at the filter screen and the breaker plate. We shall not concern ourselves here with determinations of pressure loss for different screen gauzes, this subject being dealt with exhaustively in the next paper [4]. In calculating pressure loss for breaker plates, certain idealised conditions must be assumed. The most important assumptions are:

1. Assumption that the melt flows on to the holes in the breaker plate evenly and undisturbed.

2. Stationary flow.

3. Initial disregard for elastic effects.

Irrespective of these assumptions it is, however, possible in many cases to calculate the pressure loss in advance.

As we shall demonstrate presently, one cannot disregard the elastic behaviour of the melt in the case of very short dies — which is, in effect, what the holes of a breaker plate are. The ways in which it can yet be taken into consideration will be discussed later on.

The first assumption is also partly responsible for the fact that calculated results differ from measured ones, since, in the ideal case, it applies only in the centre of a melt flow-way and then only if the rotary movement of the melt, caused by the movement of the screw, is but slight. In the peripheral zones it is no longer fulfilled.

Fixing the geometric conditions

Geometric conditions are important for the next calculations. These are explained in fig. 2.

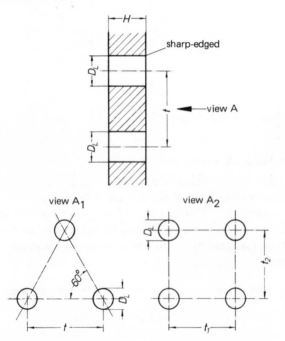

Fig. 2. Fixing the geometric conditions for breaker plates.

The centre points of the holes are normally positioned on the corner points of an equilateral triangle as shwon in A_1 in fig 2. The distance t between the centres of the holes is given by the length of a side of the triangle. It is also possible for the centre points of the holes to coincide with the corners of a rectangle or square. The distance t then results from the arithmetic means of the distances t_1 and t_2 in the two directions:

$$t = \frac{t_1 + t_2}{2}$$

Determination of pressure drop

There are two ways of calculating pressure decrease due to a breaker plate. Both have their advantages and disadvantages, depending on the particular problem.

A breaker plate is normally designed in such a way that there is the same pressure loss for each hole for a given part volume throughput. If one looks closely at the holes of a breaker plate, it will be seen that they usually have a relatively small h/D ratio (depth/diameter − length = breaker plate thickness h). The relationships given in tables and the technical literature, e. g. for a circular die

$$\frac{\Delta p}{L^*} = \frac{8\,\bar{\eta}\,V}{\pi\,R^4} \tag{3}$$

where $\bar{\eta}$ = the representative viscosity

cannot normally be applied to such short dies, since the influx effects result in an influx pressure loss which occurs in capillary rheometry and can be demonstrated, as shown for example in [5], and determined by means of the so-called Bagley correction. This influx pressure loss is caused by expansion flow, secondary flow and the conversion of the speed profile.

According to [6], it can be taken into account in computing breaker plates via an imaginary die length L^*, using equation (3):

$$L^* = (L/R_L + E)R_L \qquad L = h \tag{4}$$

The experimentally determined values for E are generally in the region of 6 for thermoplastics, according to [5] and [6]. It is advisable to use this as an approximate figure if no other details are available.

It is thus possible to arrive at an approximate design of the breaker plate. Here, we have not taken into consideration the breaker plate geometry, the number of holes and the effect these have on each other. To determine these influencing factors, the following procedure is suggested.

The pressure loss Δp_L which occurs when melt passes through a breaker plate with sharp-edged holes, is usually composed of several parts, namely

1. contraction loss due to constriction where the melt approaches the breaker plate,

2. expansion loss due to the melt stream expanding as it leaves the other side of the breaker plate, and

3. pressure loss due to shear and expansion of the melt.

In the case of polymer melts, it has been shown however, that the third part predominates over the other two by far and that these — i. e. contraction and expansion losses, representing an impulse loss, can be disregarded. Using work described in [7] as a basis, it was found that the pressure loss is essentially a function of a breaker plate constant, namely

$$K_L = Re_N \left(\frac{D_L}{h}\right) \times \left(\frac{h}{t}\right)^{0.7} \times z_L^{0.25} \tag{5}$$

A constituent of this constant is the Reynolds number Re_N (N = non-Newtonian) which is formed with the "representative" viscosity

$$Re_N = \frac{v_L D_L \, \rho}{\eta} \tag{6}$$

other constituents being the ratio of hole diameter D_L to breaker plate thickness h, the ratio of breaker plate thickness h to distance between centres of two holes t, as well as the number of holes z_L in the breaker plate.

To calculate the Reynolds number, the individual quantities should be put into equation (9) in the following dimensions:

$[v_L]$ = cm/s

$[D_L]$ = cm

$[\rho]$ = g/cm^3

$[\eta]$ = d Pa $\cdot$ s = 0.1 Pa $\cdot$ s

In this way, the correct figure for the Reynolds number will be obtained without any conversion calculations being necessary. The mean fluid velocity in the holes, necessary to form the Reynolds number, is obtained from the equation

$$\overline{V}_L = \frac{\dot{V}}{z_L \times \pi/4 \times D_L^2} \tag{7}$$

The melt density ρ should be determined at the melt temperature T and used in the calculation

$$\rho(T) = \rho(T_0) \times \frac{1}{1 + \beta(T - T_0)} \tag{8}$$

Equation (12) indicates the relationship, and table 2 contains the constants for the most commonly used materials. Reynolds numbers are determined primarily by the viscosity and vary between 10^{-6} and 10^{-3}.

Fig. 3 shows the pressure loss, standardised in relation to the back pressure $\rho V_L^2/2$ which is produced in the holes with medium fluid velocities, plotted against the breaker plate constant K_L. The continuous curve describes the pressure loss which results if one disregards the elastic influences. The functional relationship is given by

$$\rho = \frac{\Delta p}{\rho \frac{\overline{v}_L^2}{2}} = \frac{a}{K_L} \tag{9}$$

Putting the density ρ in the dimension of g/cm^3 and velocity in cm/s, gives us the pressure $[p] = dPa = 0.1$ Pa. For further conversions, the reader is referred to the table of SI units at the beginning of this book.

For Newtonian substances, $a = 100$. Fig. 3 shows the curve for $a = 100$ and this also includes figures obtained for LDPE from [8]. The difference between the continuous curve and the measured values is due to the elastic behaviour which was also determined with the measured values.

Since the quantity K_L remains constant initially and, as the entered values show, pressure loss values for a material can be approximated through a straight line in a double-logarithmic diagram, the value for a can be determined from the ratio $\zeta e/\zeta(a = 100)$.

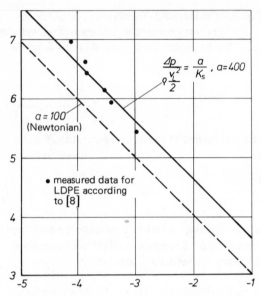

Fig. 3. Standardised pressure loss ζ as a function of the breaker plate constant K.

$$a = \frac{\zeta e}{\zeta (a = 100)} \tag{10}$$

ζe results from measured points obtained with a laboratory breaker plate of arbitrary geometry. For the approximation of the figures in fig. 3, a was found to be equal to 400 for LDPE. In this way, as described in [6], one introduces an imaginary increase of die length to determine the elastic behaviour.

The determination of the pressure loss may be explained by the following example. The data for the breaker plate are listed below:

Number of holes, z_L	37	
Hole diameter, D_L	5	mm
Breaker plate thickness, h	7	mm
Distance between hole centres, t	5.5	mm
Breaker plate diameter, D	44	mm

The material used is LDPE and the throughput $\dot{m}$ is 50 kg/h at a melt temperature ϑ of 180 °C.

Table 2. Polymer characteristics for calculating density.

$$\rho(T) = \rho(T_0) \, \frac{1}{1 + \beta(T - T_0)}$$

Polymer	$T_0/°C$	$p(T_0)/g/cm^3$	β/K^{-1}
LDPE	115	0.801	0.69×10^{-3}
HDPE	131	0.792	0.69×10^{-3}
PP	186	0.759	0.61×10^{-3}
PVC	80	1.370	0.73×10^{-3}
PS	84	1.029	0.56×10^{-3}
PC	150	1.161	$0.6 \ \times 10^{-3}$
PETP	280	1.167	0.64×10^{-3}
PMMA	105	1.155	0.58×10^{-3}
PIB	2	0.931	0.72×10^{-3}

The total volume throughput $\dot{V}$ which is necessary for determining the mean speed $\bar{v}_L$ is given by

$$\dot{V} = \frac{\dot{m}}{\rho(T)} = \frac{50 \text{ kg/h}}{0.767 \text{ g/cm}^3} = 18.1 \, \frac{cm^3}{s}$$

The density is obtained from equation (12) and table 2.

With equation (10) one obtains the mean fluid velocity $\bar{v}_L$ inside the holes as 2.5 cm/s.

To determine the "representative" viscosity $\bar{\eta}$ one needs the "representative" shear rate according to table 1. This is given by

$$\bar{\dot{\gamma}} = \frac{4}{\pi} \times \frac{\dot{V}_L}{R^3} \times 0.815 = 32.5 \text{ s}^{-1} \text{ with } \dot{V}_L = \frac{\dot{V}}{Z_L}$$

The viscosity is now obtained through making use of this shear rate with the help of one of the viscosity theorems mentioned earlier or, if available, from a flow or viscosity curve. For our example, $\bar{\eta}$ was calculated from a poly-nomial theorem and gave the value

$$\bar{\eta} = 1.375 \times 10^3 \text{ Pa.s} = 1.375 \times 10^4 \text{ dPas}$$

The breaker plate constant K_L then assumes the following value:

$$K_L = 1.45 \times 10^{-4}$$

The total pressure loss across the breaker plate is then expressed by

$$\Delta p = 6.5 \times 10^5 \text{ N/m}^2$$
$$= 6.5 \times 10^5 \text{ Pa}$$
$$= 6.5 \text{ bar}$$

Table 3. Comparison of the two methods of calculating the decrease in pressure.

No	$\dot{m}$ [kg/h]	n	Δp [bar] 8	Δp [bar] equ. (6), E=0	Δp [bar] equ. (6), E=6	Δp [bar] equ. (12)
1	25,8	7	15	3,6	11,6	19,2
2	25,8	19	10,5	2,2	7,1	10,8
3	25,8	37	6	1,8	5,8	6,0
4	50,6	7	17,5	4,8	15,1	25,2
5	50,6	19	12	3,8	12,2	12,0
6	50,6	37	6,5	3,0	9,5	6,4

Table 3 compares the two methods of calculation. The basis was formed by the determinations of [8]. It is evident that the calculation according to equation (3) with E = 6 is in relatively good agreement for the breaker plate with a small number of holes (n = 7), but shows greater deviations for larger numbers of holes. Here it is better to use equation (9) with the breaker plate constant K_L, since this takes account of mutual influences which become more marked as the number of holes increases. The advantage of carrying out calculations using the method proposed in [6] is undoubtedly that it is simple. It should be noted that the concept of representative viscosity is used for both.

Effect of inlet geometry

As fig. 2 shows, the above mentioned relationships apply to the example of a sharp-edged inlet at the breaker plate and may therefore be used to calculate maximum pressure loss.

The pressure loss at the breaker plate can be reduced by improving the inlet zone. In the simplest case, this can be achieved by rounding off the inlet or countersinking in the inlet zone. Examples of how the inlet geometry can be improved are shown in fig. 4. In this diagram are shown, from left to right, the inlet geometries which, although not so easy to achieve, will result in better flow.

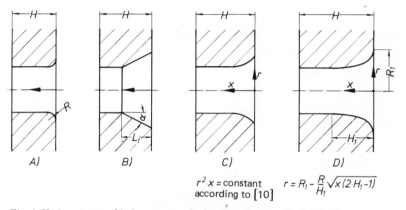

$$r^2 \cdot x = \text{constant}$$
according to [10]

$$r = R_1 - \frac{R}{H_1}\sqrt{x(2 \cdot H_1 - 1)}$$

Fig. 4. Various types of hole geometry for breaker plates on the inlet side.

Using PVC as example, the effect of the slope of a countersunk hole (fig. 4, B) on pressure loss and throughput of pelletiser dies has been demonstated in [9]. One can generally say that, by countersinking up to 30° (half the aperture angle) the pressure drop can be reduced by up to 20 %, although this varies according to the material. Larger aperture angles can, as is mentioned in [6] and experimentally shown in [11], lead to secondary vortices which tend to encourage melt deposits in these areas and do not result in any reduction of pressure.

In many cases it is best to determine pressure loss experimentally on individual breaker plates with different inlet angles.

The appearance of influx vortices can be prevented by means of complex hole designs such as those suggested in fig. 4 C and D. To achieve uniform expansion and freedom from vortices of the melt stream near the approach to the breaker plate holes, the trumpet-shaped inlet shown in fig. 4 C has been suggested in [10]. The design shown in fig. 4 D has the same purpose, the difference being that the sharp edge of fig. 4 C is avoided.

41

Guidelines on mechanical lay-out

For the purpose of mechanical lay-out, the combination of screen pack and breaker plate should be regarded as one unit. The pressure loss of the breaker plate should be kept at a minimum, bearing in mind the breaker plate's mechanical strength which is greatly reduced by the large number of holes. At the same time, the screen gauze should not buckle beyond a certain minimum near the holes where it is unsupported.

Strength calculations for the breaker plate

Geometrically, a breaker plate may be regarded as a circular disc which is subjected to flexural stresses.

According to Kirchhoff's plate theory and [12], the maximum curvature of a rigidly clamped, perforated circular plate under pressure, as shown in fig. 5, is given by

$$f_{max} = \frac{pR^4}{64N} \qquad (11)$$

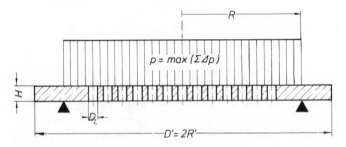

Fig. 5. Symmetrically loaded circular breaker plate.

For loads and clamping conditions different from those shown in fig. 5, further mathematical formulae are given in tabular form in [12]. The plate rigidity is given by the following expression:

$$N = \frac{E h^3}{12(1 - \nu^2)} \qquad (12)$$

In these equations, p is the pressure difference across the breaker plate and the screens, E is the modulus of elasticity, ν the transverse contraction index

42

and α the attenuation constant which describes the ratio of N/N_o of the unperforated plate to the perforated one and can be described as follows:

$$\alpha = 1 - \frac{2\,R_L}{t} \tag{13}$$

The distance between hole centres, t, is obtained as indicated in section 3.1 for different hole arrangements. In the case of unequal hole distances, as shown in fig. 2, it is expedient to base strength calculations on a medium load. If it seems necessary to calculate the loads for the solid metal in between the holes separately, this is dealt with in [12]. For practically relevant cases the minimum figure for α = 0.12. Values lower than this are meaningless.

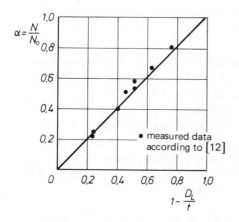

Fig. 6. Flexural strength of breaker plates according to [12].

Fig. 6 shows, by way of comparison, measured data according to [12] and the ratio N/N_o as a function of the attenuation constant. A recent analysis [19] which goes more into structural mechanical details, concludes that with this theorem it is not possible to exactly reproduce conditions for very thin and very thick plates. For thin plates the figure calculated for the deflection is too high, whilst the exact opposite is true for thick plates. The validity range of equation (13) is thus limited to

$$0.7 \leqslant \frac{h}{t} \leqslant 3$$

43

To calculate the plate thickness it is necessary to include in the calculations the relevant clamping ratio of the plate. Assuming maximum elastic flexural stress at the centre of the plate, the plate thickness is given by

$$h = B_p D \left(\frac{p \, S}{\alpha \sigma_{\text{perm.}}} \right)^{0.5} \tag{14}$$

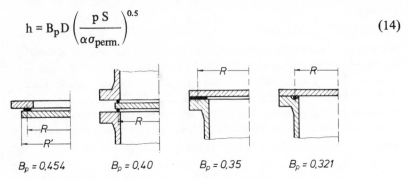

$B_p = 0.454$ $B_p = 0.40$ $B_p = 0.35$ $B_p = 0.321$

Fig. 7. Calculation factor B_p for circular plates clamped in different ways near the edge.

In this equation, the calculation factur B_p describes various peripherial clamping conditions of the plate, this factor varying between 0.454 for an unclamped plate and 0.321 for a rigidly clamped plate. The calculation of the thickness of multi-component breaker plates should be carried out in a similar manner, using a safety factor which has been increased by about 10 %. Fig. 7 provides information on chosing the calculation factor. This relationship furthermore includes the attenuation constant and the external plate diameter D which should be made equal to the mean diameter of the seal (2R) for the purpose of the calculation.

The safety factor S normally varies between 1.5 and 1.8. The maximum permissible flexural stress is denoted by σ_{perm}.

In deciding on breaker plate desing from the mechanical point of view, it is necessary to consider short-term pressure peaks in front of the breaker plate. These include:

1. Pressure peaks which appear for a short while in front of the breaker plate during starting-up and which can be two to three times as high as the differential pressures during stationary operation ($S_p = 2 - 3$).

2. Increase in pressure in front of the breaker plate caused by the screen gauzes becoming clogged. According to [13] one must here allow for an additional pressure loss Δp_{SZ} of 50 bar plus the screen pressure loss

44

Δp_S since, with such a rise in pressure, it is normally advisable to change screens. For safety's sake, this figure should be multiplied by a safety factor of $1.2 - 2$ before being used in the calculation.

For the pressure p to be put into equation (14), the maximum value of the additions of all pressure decreases across the screen and breaker plate is given by

$$p = \max\{S_p \Delta p_L + \Delta p_{SZ} + \Delta p_S\} \tag{15}$$

Determination of screen deflection

Screens or screen gauzes are mechanically supported against the differential pressure by the downstream breaker plate. The actual supporting function is achieved by the solid metal between the holes of the breaker plate. Near these holes, the screen or screen pack is subjected to flexural stresses. The size of the holes must be such that a certain maximum deflection of the screen or screen pack is not exceeded. Here, the maximum deflection depends upon the maximum permissible tensile stress for a screen gauze wire.

The geometric data necessary for further discussions are shown in fig. 8.

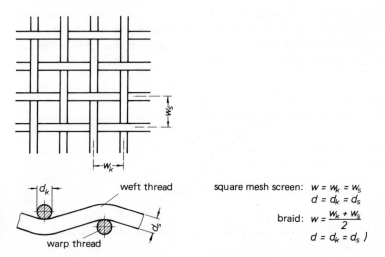

square mesh screen: $w = w_k = w_s$
$d = d_k = d_s$

braid: $w = \dfrac{w_k + w_s}{2}$
$d = d_k = d_s$)

Fig. 8. Structure of screen gauzes and braid, and expressions used.

45

To calculate the deflection of a certain portion of the screen, one uses the same method as for computing the breaker plate. The basis, here too, is Kirchhoff's plate theory. In contrast to the breaker plate however, the screen area near the holes is regarded as mobile rather than firmly clamped. The maximum curvature of the screen under the influence of the differential pressure p_s is then given by

$$f_{max} = \frac{p_s}{64} \frac{R_L}{N_s} \times \frac{5 + \nu}{1 + \nu} \tag{16}$$

The hole radius R_L forms part of this equation. If the holes are countersunk or profiled near the inlet, the maximum radius $R_{L,max}$ must be used as well as the screen rigidity N_s which is given by

$$N_s = \frac{E\, h_s^3\, \alpha_s}{12(1 - \nu^2)} \tag{17}$$

where α_s is the attenuation constant for screens and h_s the screen thickness which takes into account the displacement of the screen gauze wires according to

$$h = d_s \left(1 + \frac{d_s}{w}\right) \tag{18}$$

The attenuation constant describes the ratio N/N_{os} of a plane, unperforated plate with a thickness of h_s to the steel screen used. Fig. 9 shows the relationship between the attenuation constant α_s and the standardised free cross-sectional area of the screens

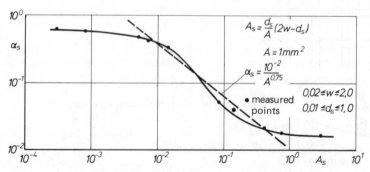

Fig. 9. Attenuation constant for calculating the strength of screen fabrics.

46

$$A_s = \frac{d_s}{A} \ (2 \ w - d) \qquad\qquad A = 1 \ mm^2$$

formed with the wire diameter d_s and mesh size w according to fig. 8.

Because of the more complex geometric relationships for screens and screen fabrics, α_s does not show a linear relationship. For an approximate determination of α_s, which is adequate in many cases, one can use the relationship

$$\alpha_s = \frac{10^{-2}}{A^{0.75}} \tag{19}$$

(dashed curve in fig. 9).

Single screens are, however, hardly ever used, screen packs composed of $3 - 5$ screens of different fineness being preferred. To calculate the deflection of these screen packs, the sum of all the separate screen stiffnesses N_s

$$N_s = \sum_{i=1}^{n} N_{si} = \frac{E}{12(1 - \nu^2)} \ \sum_{i=1}^{n} \ (h_{si}^3 \cdot \alpha_{si}) \tag{20}$$

(n being the number of screens) must be used in equation (16) as well as the total pressure decrease $\Delta p_{s, tot.}$.

To prevent the screens from bursting near the breaker plate holes, the permissible load must be ascertained. The tensile stress of a screen gauze wire is given, according to [18], by the following expression

$$\frac{\sigma_z}{S_s E} = 0.5 \left(\frac{f_{max}}{R_L} \right)^2 \tag{21}$$

This tensile stress must fulfil the condition $\sigma_{z, perm.} > \sigma_z$ Figures for $\sigma_{z, perm.}$ can be obtained from tables. In addition, it is possible to introduce a safety factor S_s for wire breakage ($1.2 \leqslant S_s \geqslant 1.5$).

Method of optimising a breaker plate

Optimising a breaker plate encompasses all the points made so far, the aim being to achieve high mechanical strength to enable the breaker plate to carry out its function of supporting the screen and minimise pressure losses.

47

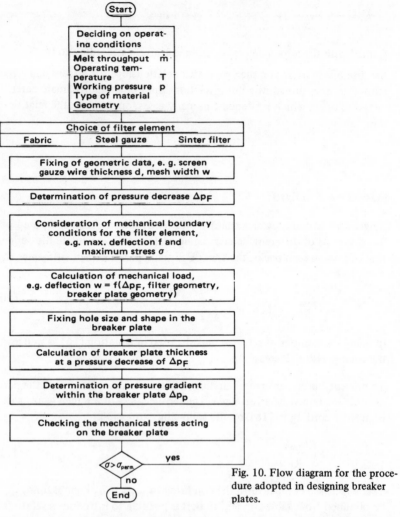

Fig. 10. Flow diagram for the procedure adopted in designing breaker plates.

The correct procedure is represented in fig. 10 in the form of a flow sheet. After deciding on the operating conditions and the type of filter element to be used, the pressure decrease Δp_s in the filtration zone is calculated. How this drop in pressure is determined is described in detail in the following paper [4]. Since this pressure decrease is much greater than that of the breaker plate, it is usually sufficient to base further calculations on the maximum pressure decrease of the filter system Δp_s.

To ascertain the most favourable hole diameter in the breaker plate one makes use of the maximum deflection of the screen or the maximum permissible tensile stress for a screen gauze wire. The hole diameter can then be determined by means of equation (21).

The number of holes in the breaker plate can be determined from

$$z_L = \frac{A}{0.866 \, t^2} \tag{22}$$

if one assumes that the hole centre points form the corners of an equilateral triangle. In this equation, A represents the area of the breaker plate which is to be drilled with holes. It is linked to the calculation of breaker plate thickness h according to equation (14). All the information needed to calculate the decrease in pressure near the breaker plate is therefore available. Calculations can be concluded at this point, depending on the nature of the particular problem. If, however, the drop in pressure near the breaker plate becomes as great as the drop in pressure in the filtration unit, i. e. the screen pack, the breaker plate thickness and pressure losses will have to be re-calculated. The necessary plate thickness is then determined iteratively.

To simplify the entire calculation one may use the nomogram shwon in fig. 11 [17]. This is divided into two parts, the first one being used for determining the hole diameter and number of holes for a given filtration system (screens). The second part is used to estimate the expected drop in pressure of the breaker plate.

The following example will illustrate how this nomogram is used.

The following information is available:

Breaker plate diameter, D	100 mm
Breaker plate thickness, h	30 mm
Volume throughput, $\dot{V}$ (already converted from mass throughput $\dot{m}$ and density T)	50 cm³/s
Viscosity (representative), η	0.9×10^3 Pa.s
Tensile strength of screen gauze wire, σ_z	100 N/mm²
Flexural strength of breaker plate, σ_b	70 N/mm²
Stiffness of screen, N_s	2300 Nmm
Pressure loss of screen, Δp_s	150 bar

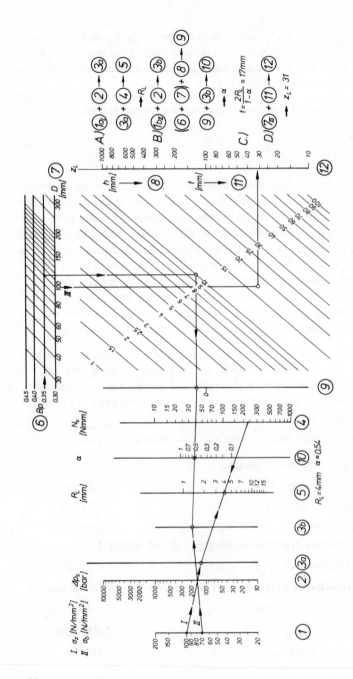

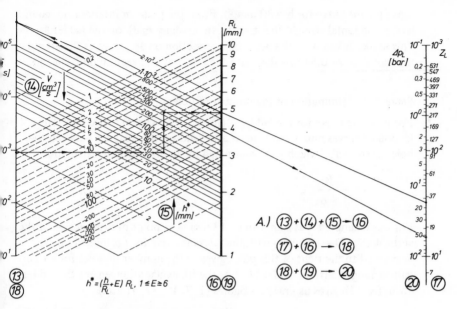

Fig. 11. Nomogram for designing breaker plates.

Solution is with the help of the nomograms (figs. 11a and 11b) in four stages, as described below.

Stage 1: Determination of hole radius R_L with fig. 11a

The tensile strength of the screen gauze wire is noted on the ladder ⑬. This point is linked directly with the pressure loss of the screen, 150 bar, on ladder ② using an auxiliary mark on ladder ③a. This is connected with the mark for screen stiffness on ladder ④ and gives us the result on ⑤, i. e. a hole radius of 4 mm.

Stage 2: Determination of the attenuation constant for the breaker plate with fig. 11a

The flexural strength of 70 N/mm² (II) is marked on ladder ⑬ and directly connected with the mark for Δp_s on ladder ②. Extending this line gives us the point of intersection with ladder ③a. The continuation starts with the combination of the value for B_p (in this example = 0.35) ⑥ and the breaker plate diamter D⑦. Vertically below this point of intersection one now

51

looks for the curve for h = 30 mm⑧. From the point of intersection, going left, a horizontal straight line gives us an auxiliary mark on the ladder⑨. This mark, linked with the point of intersection on ③b , gives us the attenuation constant of 0.54 together with the point of intersection on ladder ⑩ .

Stage 3: Determination of the number of holes z_L

For this, one looks for the ladder⑦(for B_p = 0.3) for D = 100 mm. The collection of curves underneath this is also valid for the distance between the hole centres t⑪ , which was determined by an intermediate calculation

$$t = \frac{2\,R_l}{1 - \alpha}$$

For this example t was found to be 17 mm. The point of intersection of the vertical at⑦(D = 100 mm) with the relevant curve for t is looked up. The horizontal to the right of this point gives us the number of holes for a triangular arrangement, on ladder ⑫ . For the triangular arrangement the ladder ⑰ in fig. 11b gives us practical figures (1, 7, 19, 37, 61 etc.).

Stage 4: Determination of loss of pressure Δp_L of the breaker plate

This is accomplished with the second part of the nomogram in fig. 11b. First of all, one looks for the value of viscosity on ladder ⑬ and for the curve for volume throughput of 50 cm³/s in the curves ⑭ (continuous line). The horizontal straight line to the value on ⑬ gives us a point of intersection with the curve from ⑭ . The vertical to this point intersects, in the curves ⑮ , the straight line for h* = h (in our example E = 0, h = 10 mm). The horizontal to this point of intersection marks an auxiliary point on ⑯ . One now marks the (calculated or selected) value for z_L (in our example equals to 31) on ⑰ , and connects this by means of a straight line with the previously found auxiliary mark. Extending this straight line produces a new auxiliary point on ⑱ which, linked with the value for R_L = 4 mm on ⑲ by a straight line, produces the result on ladder ⑳ , namely 56 bar.

The safety factor in this nomogram was 2 throughout.

The data relating to the breaker plate and the resultant decrease in pressure are thus known, using the information supplied. This nomogram, which was given in [17] probably does not cover every possible case and the mathematical relationships we have discussed should then be used.

Summary

We have discussed the various relationships which can be used for designing and optimising a breaker plate from the rheological and mechanical points of view. The basis for these calculations is normally the maximum drop in pressure of the entire filtration system. The supporting elements of other types of filter system, e. g. filter candles [14] can be designed in a similar manner.

Bibliography

[1] *Hensen, F.,* a. *E. Gathmann:* Kunststoffe 65 (1974), 7, pp. 343 – 349.

[2] *Schenkel, F.:* Kunststoff-Extrudertechnik. Carl Hanser Verlag, 1963.

[3] *Wortberg, J.:* Werkzeugauslegung für Ein- und Mehrschichtextrusion. Paper presented at the RWTH Aachen (D 82), 1978.

[4] *Bauer, G. Ehrmann* a. *W. Schneider:* Filtrieren von Kunststoffschmelzen. VDI-Reihe Ingenieurwissen, VDI-Verlag, Düsseldorf, 1981.

[5] *Michaeli, W.:* Extrusionswerkzeuge für Kunststoffe. Carl Hanser Verlag, München, 1979.

[6] *Knappe, W.:* Granulieren von thermoplastischen Kunststoffen. VDI-Reihe Ingenieurwissen, VDI-Verlag, 1974.

[7] *Brauer, H.:* Grundlagen der Einphasen- und Mehrphasenströmungen. Verlag Sauerländer, Aarau, 1971.

[8] *Ehrmann, G.:* Personal communication, 1981.

[9] *Franz, P.:* Granulieren von thermoplastischen Kunststoffen. VDI-Reihe Ingenieurwissen, VDI-Verlag, 1974.

[10] *Hürlimann, H. P.,* a. *W. Knappe:* Rheologica Acta 11 (1972), pp. 292/301.

[11] *Schümmer, P.,* a. *U. Werner:* Kautschuk, Gummi und Kunststoffe 19 (1966), 8, pp. 489 – 493.

[12] *Schwaigerer, S.:* Festigkeitsberechnung im Dampfkessel-, Behälter- und Rohrleitungsbau, 3. Auflage, Springer-Verlag, 1978.

[13] *Kreyenborg, U.:* Industrie-Anzeiger 95, 106 (1973), pp. 2513 – 2515.

[14] *Hensen, F.,* a. *H. Siemetzki:* Kunststoffe 70 (198), 11, pp. 753 – 758.

[15] *Münstedt, H.:* Berechnen von Extrudierwerkzeugen. VDI-Reihe Ingenieurwissen, VDI-Verlag, Düsseldorf, 1978.

[16] *Münstedt, H.:* Praktische Rheologie der Kunststoffe. VDI-Reihe Ingenieurwissen, VDI-Verlag, Düsseldorf.

[17] *Thebing, U.:* Personal communication, IKV Aachen, 1981.

[18] *Wolmir, A. S.:* Biegsame Platten und Schalen. VEB Verlag für Bauwesen Berlin, 1962.

[19] *Kempis, R. D.:* Strukturmechanische Analyse von Rohrbündeltragplatten mittels FE-Methode. Paper presented at the RWTH Aachen, 1981.

Calculation and experimental determination of the pressure losses of various screen fabrics

Wolfgang Bauer, Gerd Ehrmann and Wolfgang Schneider

Aims and objectives

In many plastics processing operations, e. g. the extrusion of thin film, blow moulding and melt spinning, increasing demands are made on the purity of the polymer melt. Processors as well as raw material producers are thus increasingly being forced to remove contaminants from their products, e. g. gel particles, pigment agglomerates or charred pieces of polymer, by filtration. For this screening to be really effective however, requires the use of fine-mesh filter elements usually several layers of them, which even in their clean state can cause considerable pressure losses. Since these pressure losses will increase more or less quickly depending on the degree of contamination, this will on the one hand cause the bursting strength of the equipment to be reached, and on the other hand produce a considerable back pressure in the machine. This means that more energy will be dissipated, the polymer will be overheated and ultimately degraded and there will be excessive build-up of free monomer. Increased pressure can also, however, lead to the fine filter screens bursting through the breaker plate holes or to contaminant particles being forced through the screen. Likewise, excessive back pressure tends to force the polymer melt back along the screw through an upstream vent. Major pressure increases are, in any case, unwelcome since they interfere with machine operation, cause throughputs to become uneconomical and necessitate frequent screen changes.

When designing filter elements one must usually consult processors or screen fabric manufacturers, since there is little information in the technical literature which would help in calculating pressure decreases in filter elements without having to determine a filter constant or similar quantity experimentally.

Starting out from the model of pipe bundles arranged in parallel or in series, with circular or rectangular pipe cross-section relationships have been derived in [1] and [2] for screen fabrics and in [3] and [4] for randomly constructed filters, with which the pressure decrease can be calculated if the filter constant – which must be experimentally determined – is constant.

Unfortunately, [1] and [2] only give figures for gases, so that it is not clear whether the formulae can also be applied to polymer melts. To calculate pressure decrease without experimentally determining filter constants, methods of calculation are given in [5] for wire cloths and in [6] for mats. These can be used, applying the power law for non-Newtonian liquids, for individual screens as well as for screen packs. The results given in [6] for oils and polyester melt deviate by a maximum of 10 % from the calculated figures. The accuracy of the method of calculating pressure losses in wire cloths [5] cannot be checked because no actual figures are available.

The purpose of the present undertaking was to work out a simple mathematical method for determining the pressure decrease in single- or multi-layer screen packs, which, if possible, would not contain any constants to be experimentally determined and which would — apart from density — require only rheological material functions. The use of a computer program based, for example, on the finite element method, was rejected on the grounds of cost.

It was also planned not to take into account the effect of some of the melt flowing in a direction parallel to the screen surface. If a screen pack/breaker plate combination is to be designed for low pressure loss, this may have to be taken into acoount.

Geometric model

In the model to be explained, it is assumed that a filter screen may be regarded as a number of identical resistances acting in parallel, i. e. the whole problem may be reduced to the mathematical determination of the pressure loss in a single mesh. When several separate screens with the same or different mesh width or wire gauge are arranged in the form of a screen pack, the pressure losses for each individual screen must be added up. In additon, one must take into account a part which makes allowances for the visco-elastic behaviour of polymer melts (see section on inlet pressure loss).

The basic thinking behind the model is to replace the mesh by a rheologically equivalent circular hole, so that the simple mathematical-physical relationships of stationary, laminar, isothermal tubular flow can be applied.

For filter screens with square meshes (only these are now under discussion) the following analogies can be applied:

Filter screen   *Alternative*

Mesh width w ⟶ hydraulic diameter D_h

Wire gauge d ⟶ length $L/2$

Filter screens have to be supported by breaker plates to give them the necessary mechanical strength. This must be borne in mind when one defines the "free" screen area through which melt flows, this being assumed as identical with the total area of the breaker plate holes (equivalent to the number of holes x cross-sectional area of one hole).

Flow behaviour of polymer melts

The flow characteristics of polymer melts can be characterised by the viscosity η which depends on shear rate as well as on pressure and temperature. The effect of the hydrostatic pressure on viscosity can, in first approximation, be neglected in the case of polyethylene, polypropylene and, within certain limits, styrene polymers, so that we only need concern ourselves with temperature and shear rate. These relationships are determined with capillary rheometers at the high shear rates appropriate for practical conditions. Various corrections have to be made in interpreting test data. Fig. 1 shows the relation between viscosity and shear rate.

To calculate flow processes it is necessary to describe these relationships by means of mathematical statements. Many relations have been published in the literature, which more or less accurately describe physical circumstances.

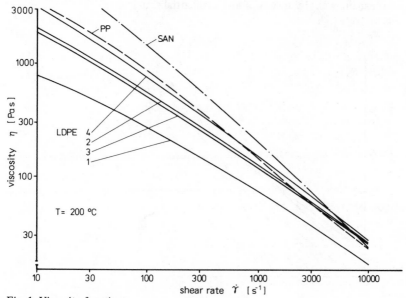

Fig. 1. Viscosity functions.

57

If one confines oneself to shear rates which are not too high, flow behaviour may be described by the power law formulated by Ostwald and de Waele:

$$\dot{\gamma} = \phi \, \tau^n \tag{1}$$

and

$$\eta = \frac{\dot{\gamma}^{\frac{1}{n} - 1}}{\phi^{\frac{1}{n}}} \tag{2}$$

For polymer melts, $n \geqslant 1$. The flow exponent n and the fluidity ϕ must be determined mathematically for the relevant part of the viscosity curve.

Inlet pressure loss

In calculating the pressure decrease in nozzles with a small L/D ratio ($\leqslant 5$) the inlet pressure loss p_c must be taken into consideration. This is due to elastic expansion and energy-dissipating flow processes in the inlet zone.

Capillary rheometry provides, as a secondary result, figures for this inlet pressure loss, fig. 2, which can be approximated as a function of shear stress τ (near the wall) by means of an exponential statement:

$$p_c = c \, \tau^m \tag{3}$$

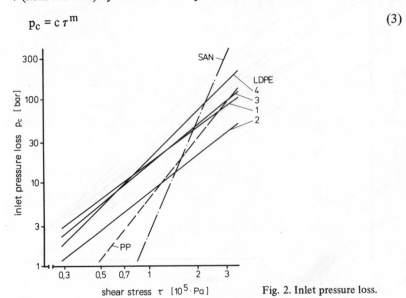

Fig. 2. Inlet pressure loss.

58

where c and m and geometry and material-specific parameters which are not dependent on temperature.

The inlet pressure losses determined with capillary rheometers relate to very big cross-sectional changes in the inlet zone (in part greater than 10 : 1) and an inlet angle of 180°. When calculating pressure losses in screens, where influx conditions are different geometrically speaking, the inlet pressure loss to be calculated cannot be taken into consideration completely but only partly. The appropriate factor ϵ must be determined experimentally.

Rheological model

In calculating laminar, isothermal tubular streams of incompressible fluids, one usually starts out from the general resistance law

$$f = \frac{64}{Re} \tag{4}$$

where f is the resistance index

$$f = \frac{2 \, \Delta p \, D_h}{\rho \, \bar{v}^2 \, L} \tag{5}$$

and Re the Reynolds number expanded for non-Newtonian liquids

$$Re = 8 \, \rho \, \bar{v}^{\,2 - \frac{1}{n}} \left[\frac{D_h \, \phi}{2(n+3)} \right]^{\frac{1}{n}} \tag{6}$$

With the geometric analogies it is possible to derive from these equations a relation for the pressure loss:

$$\Delta p = \frac{8 \, d}{w} \left[\frac{2(n+3) \, \bar{v}}{w \, \phi} \right]^{\frac{1}{n}} \tag{7}$$

In this equation, only the mean flow speed $\bar{v}$ has to be determined from the throughput:

$$\bar{v} = \frac{\dot{M}}{\rho \, F} \left(\frac{w + d}{w} \right)^2 \tag{8}$$

59

We thus obtain the equation for determining the pressure loss due to the viscosity:

$$\Delta p = \frac{8\,d}{w}\left[\frac{2(n+3)\,\dot{M}\,(w+d)^2}{\rho\,F\,\phi\,w^3}\right]^{\frac{1}{n}} \tag{9}$$

In the case of multi-layer screen packs the pressure losses for each layer, calculated using equation (9), must be added.

Starting out from equation (3), the inlet pressure loss is calculated from the following equation:

$$p_c = c\left[\frac{2(n+3)\,\dot{M}\,(w+d)^2}{\rho\,F\,\phi\,w^3}\right]^{\frac{m}{n}} \tag{10}$$

It must however be noted that this figure should only be used for fine mesh screens and there only partly (Δp_{c0}). With this, we obtain the total pressure drop as

$$\Delta p_{tot.} = \sum_i \Delta p_i + \epsilon\, p_{c0} \tag{11}$$

Determination of n and ϕ

As fig. 1 shows, the slope of the curve $\eta(\dot{\gamma})$ and thus also the flow exponent n is a function of shear rate, i. e. to determine n and ϕ, one must estimate the "operating range" of the shear rate. Here, one can use the apparent shear rate with sufficient accuracy

$$D = \frac{8\,\bar{v}}{w} \tag{12}$$

From the slope of the viscosity curve in this region, and the viscosity, one can calculate the required material parameters:

$$n = \frac{1}{\dfrac{d\lg\eta}{d\lg\dot{\gamma}} + 1} \tag{13}$$

60

$$\phi = \frac{D^{1-n}}{\eta_D^n} \tag{14}$$

Experimental set-up

In order to check the above mentioned mathematical statements, the pressure decrease in screen fabrics was experimentally determined for a number of polymer melts. The polymers chosen were LDPE, PP and SAN, table 1, which all have different viscosities and elastic properties.

Table 1. Melt flow index of the polymers examined.

Polymer	MFI [g/10 min]	Method of determining MFI [°C]	[kg]
LDPE 1	6 to 8	190	2,16
LDPE 2	1,7 to 2,2	190	2,16
LDPE 3	1,3 to 1,8	190	2,16
LDPE 4	0,1 to 0,3	190	2,16
PP	1,8	230	2,16
SAN	12	200	21,6

The main part of the experimental set-up, fig. 3, was a test nozzle in which the pressure and temperature was registered in front of the nozzle (1) as well as behind it (2). It was possible to determine the effect of the breaker plate on pressure decrease by carrying out a test without screens, the figure obtained being taken into account in the calculations.

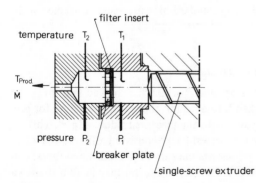

Fig. 3. Experimental set-up.

61

Table 2 contains the geometric data for the breaker plate used, and the screens examined.

Table 2. Geometric data for breaker plate and screen.

Breaker plate: 37 holes, 5 mm in diameter breaker
plate thickness 7 mm

screen:	w[μm]	d[μm]
	40	32
	80	56
	250	160
	800	500

When melt flows through the screen and breaker plate, the melt temperature increases from T_1 to T_2. Since isothermal flow was assumed in deriving the above mathematical relationships (the calculation of non-isothermal flow is very much more complicated and economically not feasible), one may make use of the mean temperature as reference temperature:

$$\overline{T} = \frac{T_1 + T_2}{2}$$

The temperature measured at the nozzle exit is less suitable for this purpose since – because of energy dissipation in the nozzle – it is higher than the temperature T_2 behind the screen. Differences of up to 10 K are possible, depending on the product and operating conditions.

The pressure was determined using standard pressure gauges suitable for the expected pressure levels.

Comparison of experiment and calculation

Interpretation of the test series obtained for LDPE 3 showed that if the inlet pressure loss was not taken into account, the calculated values for pressure drop were too low compared with the measured values, fig. 4. This applies to single screens as well as screen packs consisting of several layers, where the total pressure loss represents the sum of the individual values calculated according to equation (9). The reason for this may be that there was

62

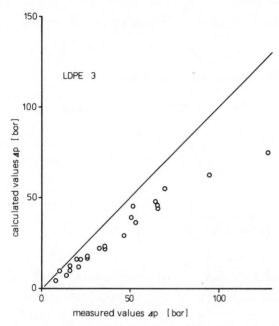

Fig. 4. Comparison of measured and calculated results without taking p_c into consideration.

too much simplification in producing the geometric and the rheological model. The assumptions made are, however, maintained with a view to practical usefulness.

If one takes the inlet pressure loss into consideration however, the question arises as to how the factor ϵ equation (11) is to be chosen. If several layers of screen fabric are used, the inlet pressure loss is considered only for the screen with the finest mesh.

Adapting the calculated values to the test results produces figures for ϵ which vary between 0 (PP) and 0.25 (LDPE 2). It would be easiest to work with only one value for ϵ and the figure of 0.2 has proved to be quite useful for the range of products examined. Figs. 5 − 8 show the relevant comparisons between measured and calculated results for ϵ = 0.2. If this figure proves to be insufficiently accurate for any given instance, appropriate tests will have to be carried out to determine an accurate figure for ϵ.

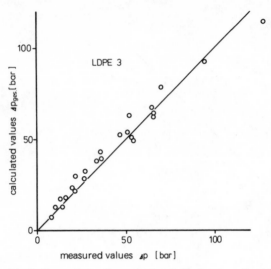

Fig. 5. Comparison of measured and calculated results, taking p_c into account ($\epsilon = 0.2$).

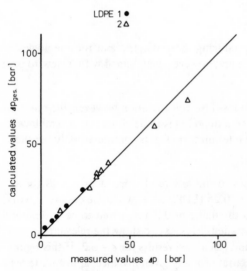

Fig. 6. Comparison of measured and calculated results, taking p_c into account ($\epsilon = 0.2$).

64 .

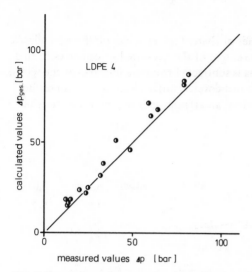

Fig. 7. Comparison of measured and calculated results, taking p_C into account ($\epsilon = 0.2$).

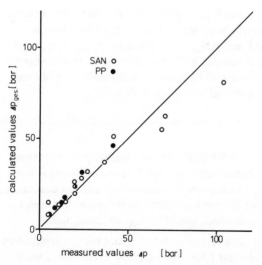

Fig. 8. Comparison of measured and calculated results, taking p_C into account ($\epsilon = 0.2$).

65

Dirt deposition on screens

The deposition of dirt, particles of charred material etc. on the screen leads to increased pressure loss. The extent of this pressure loss can be estimated if the dirt-covered surface area is subtracted from the free area of the screen, F. Determining the size of the dirt-covered surface is, however, almost impossible in practice. Nevertheless, an attempt is made in fig. 9, to what

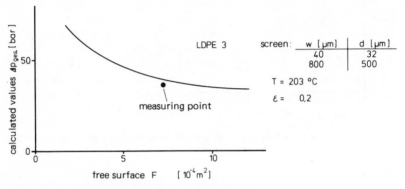

Fig. 9. Effect of free screen area F on pressure loss Δp_{tot}.

extent the remaining free surface F takes part in the pressure drop. Because of the non-Newtonian flow characteristics of polymer melts, there is no linear relationship between F and Δp_{tot}. In actual fact, Δp_{tot}. will rise less markedly when the screen is covered with dirt, because increased energy dissipation will cause the viscosity to be reduced additionally – isothermal conditions were, of course, assumed in the calculations.

Summary

The exact calculation (e. g. with the finite element method) of the pressure drop of polymer melts in screens, with due consideration of the non-Newtonian flow characteristics of such melts, is cumbersome and not economically feasible. The purpose of the work described in this paper has been to develop mathematical methods which would be easy to accomplish.

Taking a geometrical model as basis, in which the square mesh is replaced by a rheologically equivalent circular hole, the following assumptions were made in producing a mathematical basis:

bore: D_h = w and L = 2 d

stationary, laminar, *isothermal* tubular flow

free screen area identical with free cross-section of breaker plate

in the case of several screens, the total pressure decrease is given by the sum of the separate pressure decreases

consideration of the inlet pressure loss but in the case of several layers only for the screen with the finest mesh.

A fairly good agreement between experiment and calculation (mean deviation about 16 %) was achieved in the present tests for the entire range of products when the inlet pressure loss, as obtained through rheometry, is taken into consideration only to an extent of 20 % (ϵ = 0.2). If this agreement is insufficient however, the factor ϵ must be determined separately for the product concerned. Ignoring the inlet pressure loss usually produces values that are too low compared with measured results.

Nomenclature

c	factor for calculating p_c according to equation (3)
d	wire gauge
D	apparent shear rate according to equation (12)
D_h	hydraulic diameter of one mesh
f	resistance factor
F	permeable screen area
L	length of alternative bore
m	exponent for calculating p_c according to equation (3)
$\dot{M}$	melt throughput through screen
n	flow exponent according to Ostwald/de Waele
p_c	inlet pressure loss
Δp	viscosity-related pressure drop
$\Delta p_{tot.}$	total pressure drop in screen according to equation (11)
Re	Reynolds number
$T_{1,2}$	melt temperature upstream and downstream from the screen
$\bar{T}$	mean melt temperature
$\bar{v}$	mean flow rate in a single mesh
w	mesh width
$\dot{\gamma}$	shear rate
ϵ	factor in equation (10)

η	viscosity
η_D	viscosity at the apparent shear rate D
ρ	density
τ	shear stress
ϕ	fluidity of the flow law according to Ostwald/de Waele

Bibliography

[1] *Blass, E.:* Chemie-Ing.-Techn. 36 (1964), 747.

[2] *Armour, J. C.,* a. *J.N. Cannon:* AIChE-Journal 14 (1968), 415.

[3] *Brignac, E. P.,* a. *W. J. Marks:* Filtration and Separation 14 (1977), 362.

[4] *Hensen, F.,* a. *H. Siemetzki:* Kunststoffe 70 (1980), 753.

[5] *Carley, J. F.,* a. *W. C. Smith:* Pol. Engng. Sci. 18 (1978), 408.

[6] *Kaplan, S. J., C. D. Morland* a. *S. C. Hsu:* Chem. Engng. 86 (1979), 93.

Slide plate system with mechanical seals

Hans-Otto Strohschein

In most slide plate systems, a seal inside a sealing ring is pressed against a slide plate on the upstream side. Thereby transferring the contact pressure through the slide plate to the thrust ring on the downstream side. The whole system is integrated with the screen changer body. The slide plate has two operating positions and can be shifted from one position to the other manually, pneumatically or hydraulically.

We shall now discuss in more detail three important components of the slide plate screen changer, namely the seals, guide ring and slide plate.

Seals

In nearly all slide plate systems there are no leak problems with the seal on the downstream side, whose contact pressure comes from mechanical clamping and from the melt pressure acting on the breaker plate. The pressure acting on the downstream side seal during operation is therefore higher than that acting on the upstream seal, making it more leakproof.

This screen area moreover does not lie in the filtration zone and cannot therefore be damaged by separated metal particles when the slide plate is moved. For this reason we shall only concern ourselves with the downstream seal. Some important structural features are

– type of sealing system used

– sealing material

– surface treatment of the seal and slide plate

– degree of precision with which all parts in contact with the seal have been machined.

Let us compare a wide, thick melt seal with a smooth bore, made of an non-copper alloy, fig. 1 B, with an improved, narrow, thin seal made of a copper alloy, with a curved lip, fig. 1 A .

69

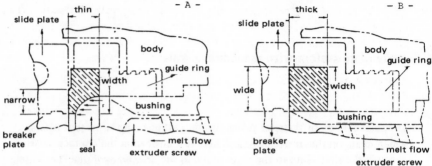

Fig. 1. Sliding plate systems for screen changers
A: narrow upstream seal made of copper alloy with curved lip
B: wide upstreams seal made of non-copper alloy with smooth throughflow bore

Type of sealing system used

The Beringer seal is the result of very extensive tests on mechanical tension caused by the guide ring and contact pressure through the melt pressure. The narrow melt seal, fig. 1A, can be operated with less mechanical contact pressure than the wider seal shown in fig. 1B. The seal with the curved lip was fitted to the screen changer in its original design and caused the screen changer to remain leakproof without the necessity of constant re-adjustment during operation. In the type A screen changer it permits tensioning with very low pressure and little post-tensioning. The other type of seal, with the smoot bore, has to absorb the whole of the contact pressure via the guide ring.

With melt seal A, an additional contact pressure is immediately produced as soon as melt flows through the screen changer, this being due to the melt pressure which acts on the curved lip sealing face. Because this force acts on the external diameter and there is a considerable projection zone, an additional, very large force acts on the seal. This forces the upstream (i. e. melt inlet) seal against the slide plate, thereby increasing the sealing force. In other words, the guide ring can be subjected to less pressure. The seal with the curve increases the contact pressure as soon as melt flows through the sealing head, thereby guaranteeing a perfect seal.

Another important advantage of this seal is that the contact pressure builds up and decreases automatically. When the melt pressure increases due to the screen becoming dirty, the contact pressure at the seal also rises. When the

70

screen is changed, this contact pressure drops. If higher sealing pressures are required, e. g. because of higher melt pressure, this self-adjustment brings major advantages. The screen changer can be operated at minimum setting pressure and force, thereby prolonging the working life of the seal.

With this type of upstream seal it is advisable to allow the extruder screw to protrude through the adaptor into the screen changer, the screw tip being about 25 mm distant from the slide plate, fig. 1 A. Since the screw is taken to within 25 mm of the slide plate, the amount of melt in this part of the screen changer is reduced. The flow rate of the polymer melt is increased and helps to keep the seal clean, so that no polymer can be deposited. Even if the screw cannot be taken so far into the screen changer body the unit functions perfectly, except in the case of very heat sensitive polymers for which screen changers with slide plates are unsuitable.

Apart from seal shape, the seal thickness is also important. Most seals are supported by a guide ring made of heat treated tool steel and sufficiently strong to act as a guide for the seal. No manufacturer of screen changers works without a stabilising support for the seal. Many year's experience has shown that an aluminium-bronze seal does not constantly become deformed.

Fig. 2. Steam heated screen changer.

Fig. 3. Electrically heated screen changer.

It follows that a properly fitted, thick enough seal will ensure trouble-free operation.

Figs. 2 and 3 show a steam and an electrically heated screen changer in which one can easily see how the guide ring presses the seal against the slide plate.

In selecting a material for the seal it is much more difficult to obtain a good seal with a material having an elastic modulus of 29×10^6 than with one having a lower elastic modulus. The aluminium-bronze seal shown in fig. 1 A has a modulus of 16×10^6 and can far more easily balance out minor damage than a material with a higher modulus, because bronze is more readily compressible than steel. By using this softer metal, leaks can be reduced or even prevented altogether. If a leak occurs when using a seal with a much higher modulus, little can be achieved by increasing the pressure, since such a sealing material will not be deformed. Furthermore, the seal width has only a linear effect in flow calculations, i. e. that a seal which is double the width will reduce leakage by half. If a leak nevertheless occurs, the seal must either be re-adjusted or replaced. Aluminium-bronze seals can be re-adjusted and their life extended through a process of "self-renewal". A steel seal on the other hand would have to be exchanged.

72

Guide ring

A wider seal (as shown in fig. 1 B) without the curved lip shown in fig. 1 A requires far higher clamp forces.

As fig. 4 shows, two hydraulics rams apply an almost tangential force to the guide ring — one from above, one from below. These rams can, of course, be used for loosening the guide ring.

To achieve absolute precision in the guides for the seals and guide rings, the screen changer body is drilled and machined without altering its position. To prevent additional tolerances, the thread of the guide rings is cut direct into the screen changer body. All these operations must be carried out with extreme care to keep tolerances as low as possible.

Fig. 4.
Guide ring with
hydraulic ram.

Slide plate

Slide plates are made from high quality tool steel, a process which involves numerous operations, e. g.

rough and fine machining

heat treatment

73

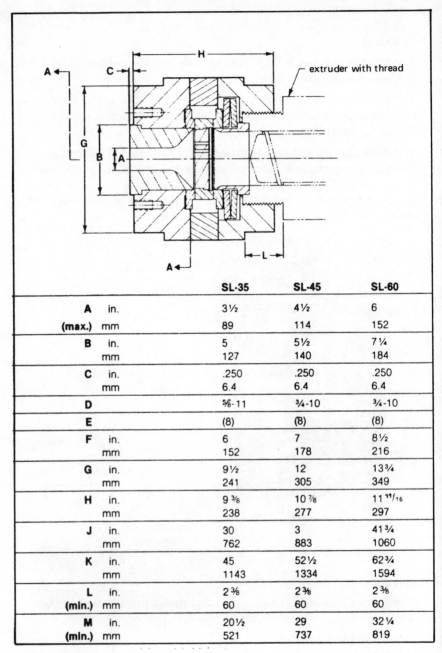

		SL-35	SL-45	SL-60
A	in.	3½	4½	6
(max.)	mm	89	114	152
B	in.	5	5½	7¼
	mm	127	140	184
C	in.	.250	.250	.250
	mm	6.4	6.4	6.4
D		⅝-11	¾-10	¾-10
E		(8)	(8)	(8)
F	in.	6	7	8½
	mm	152	178	216
G	in.	9½	12	13¾
	mm	241	305	349
H	in.	9 ⅜	10 ⅞	11 ¹¹/₁₆
	mm	238	277	297
J	in.	30	3	41¾
	mm	762	883	1060
K	in.	45	52½	62¾
	mm	1143	1334	1594
L	in.	2⅜	2⅜	2⅜
(min.)	mm	60	60	60
M	in.	20½	29	32¼
(min.)	mm	521	737	819

Fig. 5. Self-locking seal.

74

hardening

annealing

post-annealing

further fine machining

chromium plating

sintering to prevent embrittlement

grinding of both sides of the slide plate

finishing, lapping of both sides of the slide plate.

Disc spring seals

Fig. 5 shows a new type of self-locking seal which will permit operating pressures of 530 bar. This design requires no manual adjustment by the operator. The advantages of this system are:

pre-adjustable, self-adjusting sealing mechanism which guarantees maximum reliability without supervision by the operator;

because the breaker plates are oversize, the screen can be used for longer periods between two screen changes;

direct barrel coupling makes the use of an adaptor unnecessary;

screws can be changed more quickly and easily without having to dismantle the entire screen changer.

Method of operation

The self-sealing screen changer, fig. 6, has been designed for direct coupling to the extruder barrel. It can be screwed direct to the threaded end of the

Fig. 6. Self-sealing screen changer.

extruder or fitted via an adaptor. Fitting can be horizontal or vertical without the screen changer having to be supported.

The contact force of the two seals acting on the slide plate is produced by the screws holding the body on the downstream side against that on the upstream side. Disc springs keep the sealing force constant, independently of the screws' clamp force or seal wear.

The disc spring tensioning device for the maximum expected pressure can very easily be changed during the fitting of the screen changer to the extruder. With this type of design the braker plates can be over-dimensioned by 25—40 % since there is a smooth throughflow bore. This enables longer production times to be achieved between successive screen changes.

Thermally insulated slide bar systems

Friedrich Lambertus

The following factors were deemed of special importance with regard to the screen changer made by Werner & Pfleiderer which incorporates a slide bar which is thermally insulated from the housing:

Reliable, maintenance-free and abrasion resistant sealing of the filtration compartment.

Avoidance of product contamination when changing screens.

Flow channel design to permit good melt flow.

Possibility of using it even at high throughputs and constant pressure loss in the screen support.

Structural features and mode of action

The slide bar is arranged at right angles to the melt stream, inside the screen changer, fig. 1. It is made with two holes to fix the filter element support plate and the filter elements themselves, these being called the filter chambers. One of these is immersed in the melt stream. Moving it from one position to another is accomplished by an hydraulic cylinder flanged on the housing from the side, this being done so quickly that the operation of the extruder and pelletising unit need not be interrupted. The energy required for this movement is produced within a few minutes by a relatively small hydraulic pump, stored in a pressure reservoir and quickly released via a suitable valve.

The housing as well as the slide are nitrided and designed to be heated by a suitable fluid or steam. The cooling plates, which are also nitrided, are normally cooled with demineralised water.

The method of sealing the filtration chamber is new, fig. 2. The melt entering between the slide and cooling plate via the narrow slit between the slide and the barrel bore is solidified in the so-called sealing slit. The sealing effect is enhanced by the shrinkage of the cooling plate bore due to a reduction in temperature, during which the slit is reduced from about 0.1 mm to a few hundredths of a mm — in some places even so much that there is metallic contact.

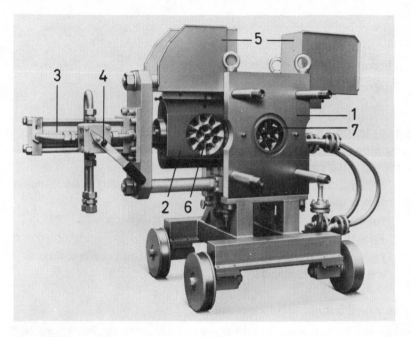

Fig. 1. Type SWZ 1200 screen changer.

1 housing
2 slide bar plate
3 hydraulic cylinder
4 change-over valve

5 protective hood
6 filter unit
7 melt inlet

The use of these units in the processing of PE, PP and PS has shown that a perfect seal is achieved and that the slide plate can be moved even if the cooling plate is cool.

An advantage which should not be underestimated is that there is less contamination of the product when changing screens. In all screen changers which are sealed via sealing rings, the melt flow-way is opened after a slight displacement. This causes the melt, which is under pressure, to be relieved and hurls individual foreign particles into the space between the slide and the housing. Since this space is not easily accessible for cleaning, the adhering melt chars and, when the screen is changed again, reaches the filtration chamber, thereby contaminating the product.

As fig. 2 shows, no deposits can be formed in the design involving thermal insulation, because of the tight fit of the slide along the entire barrel width.

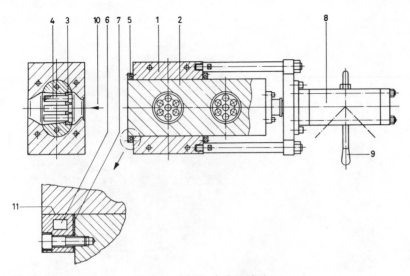

Fig. 2. Diagram of a screen changer with thermal insulation.

1 housing	7 thermal insulation plate
2 slide bar plate	8 hydraulic cylinder
.3 supporting plate	9 lever for change-over valve
4 filter element	10 melt inlet
5 cooling plate	11 thermal sealing gap
6 cooling channel	

Residual melt which has escaped during screen changing due to the above described melt pressure relief can be easily scraped off the front of the cooling plates. Any contaminant adhering to the circumference of the outer half of the slide bar is stripped when the cooling plate is moved.

Another way of avoiding product contamination is the exchange of the complete filtration unit, consisting of screens and screen supports, i. e. breaker plates, against a clean assembly. In the above described design, this can be easily achieved with cylindrical elements — to be described in more detail below — thanks to the relatively small size and the relatively light weight, even in the case of large screens.

Another distinguishing feature of this screen changer, besides the thermal insulation, is the cylindrical shape of the filter screens, fig. 3. Instead of the flat screens normally used in slide bar systems, cylindrical units consisting of a supporting basket with filter insert are used. The filter insert is normally in two layers, consisting of a supporting fabric and the actual

79

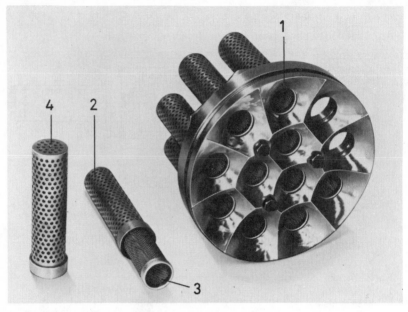

Fig. 3. Filter element supporting plate with filter elements.
1   filter element support plate
2   supporting basket
3   filter insert
4   filter element

screen fabric. The screen changer sizes differ in the number of filter elements they contain, not in their size. The following advantages result:

lower pressure loss, unaffected by the size of the filtration unit, of the screen fabric support;

improved flow conditions, thanks to much reduced expansion of the melt flow-way;

smaller product volume and therefore much faster heating up of the product and much shorter residence time;

smaller and more compact construction for the same screen area, resulting in less expensive production;

easier to handle, due to lighter weight.

There is, however, the disadvantage that the filters are more expensive to produce, although this is largely compensated by the fact that large quantities of these filters can be produced less expensively, as well as by the fact that screen material is saved because the screen isert only has two layers. Moreover, the filters can be used several times by being cleaned with the Jet Cleaner made by Beringer or by the Procedyne bath made by Schwing, followed by tratment in an ultrasonic bath.

Table 1. Sizes and technical data.

Size		SWZ 700	SWZ 1200	SWZ 1900	SWZ 2700
Total screen area	cm²	700	1200	1900	2700
Number of filter elements		7	12	19	27
Permissible melt pressure in front of the screen	bar	350			
Permissible pressure difference at the screen	bar	200			
Time required to push screen through	sec	1			
Type of heating		steam or heat transfer fluid			
Permissible pressure of heating medium	bar	40			
Required heating capacity heating-up operation	kW kW	17 5	30 9	45 13	55 17
Drive capacity of hydraulic pump	kW	2,2	2,2	4	4
Operating pressure (hydraulic)	bar	140 to 175			
Reservoir volume (hydraulic)	dm³	30	30	2x30	
Throughput range		2 to 7	3 to 12	5 to 19	7 to 27
Weight	kg	540	1000	1400	1800

The type designation, e. g. SWZ 700 oval, is the abbreviated designation for a screen changer with cylindrical filter elements which are accomodated in a slide bar with oval cross-section. The screen area for this size is 700 cm².

81

Screen changing systems with hydraulic seals

Eberhard Uhland

Demands made on the screen changing system

Discontinuous screen changing systems normally have a screen carrier which is positioned at right angles to the melt stream. This accomodates the screen inserts (screen fabric) and can be designed as a flat side bar. The following demands must be met for the system to function properly:

Reliable sealing of the screen carrier against too high a melt pressure 300 – 400 bar) at too high a temperature and with low viscosity melts. The seal should remain effective also after many screen changing operations.

Prevention of wear of the sealing faces.

The screen changing operation must be carried out as quickly and easily as possible. The extruder or melt pump should not have to be switched off. It should also be possible to push the screen carrier through quickly.

The pressure decrease in the screens and breaker plates should be as low as possible.

The space in which the polymer melt flow should be designed for easy flow and the melt should remain inside the screen changer for as short a time as possible. Dead spots should always be avoided so as to prevent melt accumulations and charring.

Screen inserts and screen carriers should be easily exchanged.

It should be possible to heat the screen changers electrically, with steam or with a heat transfer fluid. Where there is a risk of explosion, the necessary safety precautions should be taken as regards heating and control.

The screen changer itself as well as the screen changing operation should be designed so that there is no risk of accident.

The above conditions may be met by using a screen changer with an hydraulically operated sealing system.

Principle of operation

The principle of a screen changer with hydraulically operated seal is shown in fig. 1. The screen carrier with the screen pack is firmly clamped between two rings during the screen changing operation, the sealing ring being forced hydraulically against the screen carrier. The contact force and thus the pressure acting on the surface between the sealing ring and thrust ring and the screen carrier, can be set via the hydraulic pressure in accordance with requirements, so that an efficient and reliable seal is achieved.

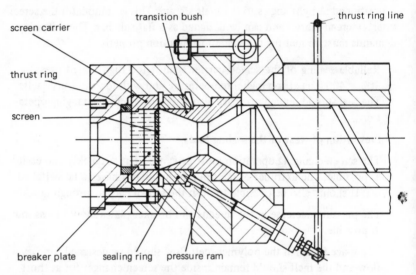

Fig. 1. Screen changer with hydraulic seal.

When the screen is changed, the hydraulic pressure is relieved, so that the sealing ring suddenly becomes detached from the screen carrier. Screen changing takes place immediately afterwards, i. e. the screen carrier with the new screen is moved hydraulically, at high speed, into the new operating position. After this has been accomplished, the sealing ring is again hydraulically forced against the screen carrier, thereby once more effecting a good seal. Since the various stages occur one after the other, electrohydraulically controlled, the entire changing-operation takes only about 0.5 to 1.5 seconds, so that the extruder or melt pump need not be switched off whilst the screen is being changed.

84

In pelletising systems for example, where the pellets are cut immediately the extruded strands leave the pelletiser die (e. g. under water pelletisation or water-cooled die face pelletisation), the screen can be changed without production being interrupted. In strand pelletisation, tearing of the strands can only be avoided however by making the distance between the screen and the strand die as long as possible, i. e. having a maximum melt volume.

Constructional details

The housing of the screen changer, see figs. 2 and 3, which is usually flanged on to the extruder, is made of high temperature resistant cast steel and is designed so as to absorb the forces produced by the melt pressure. It can also be connected to different dies.

The plate-like screen carrier, which is pushed horizontally and hydraulically through the housing whilst the screen is being changed, contains two openings to accomodate the breaker plates. During screen changing, the screen carrier is guided at the top and bottom by means of guide rails in the housing, and on the left an right through the thrust and sealing ring. The design is such that the screw can be withdrawn from the extruder without the screen changer having to be dismantled.

Fig. 2. Screen changer with hydraulic seal, seen from the extruder side.

Fig. 3. Screen changer with hydraulic seal, seen from the die side.

Table 1. Basic technical data for screen changer with hydraulic seal.

Model	Screen diameter mm	screen area cm²	number of holes Pl. 1	number of holes Pl. 2	hole diameter Pl. 1	hole diameter Pl. 2	
SW 90	90	63,6	55	–	9	–	
SW 120	120	113	96	–	9	–	
SW 150	150	177	140	–	9	–	
SW 200	200	314	225	–	9	–	
SW 250	250	491	356	–	9	–	
SW 300	300	707	600	86	7	24	
SW 400	400	1288	876	124	8	25	
SW 450	450	1520	1100	154	8	25	
SW 500	500	1964	1414	202	8	24	

The screen or screen pack fitted to the screen carrier is supported by a breaker plate designed to withstand the melt pressures produced on the one hand and on the other to keep flow resistance to a minimum. In the large models (from SW 300 upwards) a two-part breaker plate is used, consisting of a thin plate with many small holes to support the screen pack and a thicker plate with large holes and very low flow resistance to absorb the forces produced. Screen area, number of holes and hole diameter for the different model are listed in table 1, which also gives the total resistance W_G and resistance per hole W_B, calculated according to the following equation:

$$W_B = \frac{128\, L_B}{\pi D_B{}^4}$$

The screen pack, consisting of a number of screens with different mesh sizes (e. g. 400, 144 and 49 meshes/cm^2) is clamped in front of the breaker plate and can be easily removed from the screen carrier and replaced by a new pack.

The sealing unit on the screen carrier consists of the thrust ring, the sealing ring and the associated hydraulic system, the latter also serving as a means of moving the screen carrier and being equipped with an accumulator.

Breaker plate						
hole lenght		free hole area cm^2		resistance/hole cm^{-3}		total resistance cm^{-3}
Pl. 1	Pl. 2	Pl. 1	Pl. 2	Pl. 1	Pl. 2	
28	–	35	–	174	–	3.164
40	–	61	–	248	–	2.583
40	–	89	–	248	–	1.771
55	–	143	–	342	–	1.520
66	–	226	–	410	–	1.152
9	75	231	389	153	9,2	0.362
12	85	440	609	119,4	8,9	0.208
12	95	550	750	119,4	9,9	0.173
15	105	711	914	149,2	12,9	0.169

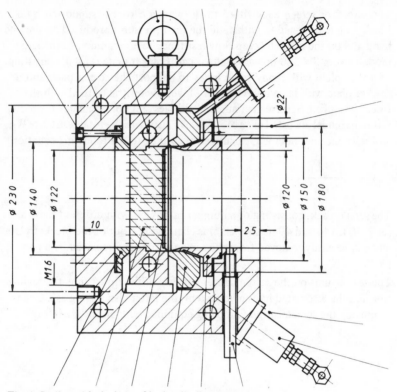

Fig. 4. Sealing with the help of hydraulically operated rams.

Two types of design are used to transfer the hydraulic pressure to the thrust ring. Fig. 4 shows one design in which hydraulically operated rams are arranged in a ring around the screen changer, each ram being equidistant from the next. Their job is to press the sealing ring against the screen carrier during sealing, the screen carrier in turn being pressed against the thrust ring. Since the rams are linked to each other by a thrust ring line, fig. 2, the pressure they exert — and therefore the sealing effect — is uniform throughout the entire circumference.

In the second design, fig. 5, the hydraulic pressure acting in a ring-shaped pressure chamber sealed with metal bellows is transferred to the thrust ring via a thrust unit.

There are no sealing problems, since the bellows can be welded to the ring-shaped housing of the pressure chamber as well as to the thrust unit. To

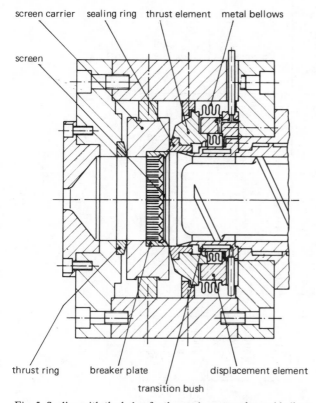

screen carrier   sealing ring   thrust element   metal bellows

screen

thrust ring   breaker plate   displacement element

transition bush

Fig. 5. Sealing with the help of a thrust element and metal bellows.

keep the volume of oil down to a minimum, a displacement element is built into the pressure chamber. This reduces the change in volume of the hydraulic pressure medium caused by the change in temperature, so that the required compensating tank can also be kept small.

The contact pressure between the sealing faces can be adjusted via the pressure in the hydraulic system and can be matched to the pressure of the polymer melt.

The sliding movement of the sealing ring on the transition bush is only very slight, amounting to only a few tenths of a mm. By selecting two suitable materials, both parts can be easily assembled. At operating temperatures however, an absolutely tight seal between transition bush and sealing ring is assured, thanks to the light press fit.

Table 2. Summary of models in the range.

| Model | screen diameter (mm) | Screen changer Dimensions (mm) | | | heating capacity (kW) | motor capacity (kW) | Hydraulics accumulator volume (l) | amount of oil necessary per stroke (l) |
		lenght	width	height				
SW 90	90	200	940	270	3.0	0.55	4	0.1
SW 120	120	235	1120	325	6.0	0.55	4	0.2
SW 150	150	400	1870	500	17.0	1.2	5	0.5
SW 200	200	470	2200	570	22.0	1.5	10	1.3
SW 250	250	515	1580	630	30.0	2.2	20	2.3
SW 300	300	700	2800	800	37.0	3.0	20	2.8
SW 400	400	700	3570	900	50.0	3.5	20	3.6
SW 450	450	700	3780	1100	55.0	4.0	35	5.0
SW 500	500	880	4325	1300	60.0	4.0	35	5.7

Fig. 6. Screen changer on strainer used to screen PVC.

Fig. 7. Screen changer SW 500 500/600 fitted to a KE 600 x 24D extruder used for pelletising PE. Output: 23,000 kg/h.

The screen changers can be heated electrically with resistance heaters, by means of steam or a heat transfer fluid. Both the housing as well as the screen carrier are heated.

A pressure gauge with signal and switch-off contact can be incorporated in the screen changer to keep a check on the amount of foreign particles which have accumulated in the screen as well as to protect the whole extrusion line. It is also possible to incorporate bursting discs with disconnecting in the screen changer.

Sizes and technical data

The range includes screen changers with screen diameters of 90 – 500 mm. The screen diameter normally corresponds to the extruder diameter. In order to avoid too frequent screen changes, it is possible to use a screen changer with a larger diameter screen, i. e. a larger screen area. Screen areas and important technical data for the breaker plates in the range are given in table 1. Table 2 shows the dimensions and heating capacities of the screen changers, as well as various data concerning the associated hydraulic systems.

Fields of use

Screen changing systems with hydraulic seals are used in the production, processing and recycling of plastics. Because of their fast action (0.5 – 1.5 seconds) they are used mainly where changing screens must not cause interruption of the extrusion process or operation of the melt pump.

Typical fields of application include:

production of granular compounds (e. g. PE, PS, PMMA, PIB, PVC), figs. 6 and 7

compounding (e. g. PP and nylon)

production of pigment concentrates (e. g. PE + 40 % carbon black)

production of expanded PS sheeting

compounding of PVC for the calandering of film and sheeting

recycling of shredded film offcuts (e. g. PE, expanded PS).

Slide bar systems with stuffing box or slot seals

Horst Köching

General requirements

The filtration of polymer melts is becoming increasingly important in the manufacture and processing of plastics. There are three basic areas where filtration is important: in the manufacture of the basic polymer, in polymer processing and in recycling.

All these areas concern thermoplastic materials. Both the filter quality as well as the design of the filtration units are governed by the type of polymer and end product quality requirements.

Production requirements demanded increasingly fine-mesh filter fabrics and screen changers which would allow the spent filter to be exchanged quickly. In the interests of economy, different types of filtration units are used for the different applications. Filtration systems with stuffing box or slot seals are suitable for all polymers and applications. Because of their different methods of manufacture and formulations, different types of polymers require filters with special design and material-specific features. If one also takes the different polymer viscosities into account and the construction of the whole manufacturing plant, a whole range of data result, which govern the choice of the screen changer. Filter manufacturers send out questionnaires to obtain the data required to select the most suitable filter for a particular application. This simplifies matters for the processor. The following data are required:

Viscometric quantities
    dynamic viscosity Pa · s
    kinematic viscosity m^2/s
    description of viscosity [1]

Test specification − melt flow index
    MFI in g/10 min according to DIN 53735, ISO/DIS 1133-69 and ASTM D 1238-73.

93

An important condition is that the screen changer must be absolutely leak proof. To keep the pressure loss due to the incorporation of a screen changing unit as low as possible, the melt flow-ways inside the screen changer should be designed so as to ensure smooth flow. The volume of all the flow channels influences the residence time of the material inside the screen changer and must be carefully considered in the case of certain kinds of material. The screen changer is selected according to the application and degree of contamination, as detailed below.

a) For discontinuous operation, i. e. for the time it takes to exchange a spent screen against a clean one, production must be interrupted.

Type D-SWE see fig. 1

Type HS see fig. 2

b) For continuous operation, i. e. there is no break in production when the screen is changed, so that there is no interruption of the melt stream.

Type K-SWE see fig. 3

Type L-SWE

With screen changers designed for continuous operation there is another difference. Contamination of the screen causes the pressure to rise continuously. The resultant difference in pressure between the contaminated and the clean screens leads to output fluctuations. Since, after the new screen has been fitted, there will be a drop in melt pressure, adjustments will have to be made whilst the pressure is increasing as well as after the screen has been changed.

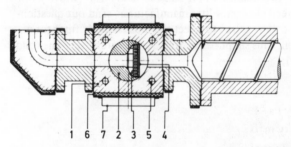

Fig. 1. Type D-SWE screen changer for discontinuous operation.
1 screen changer housing
2 screen bush
3 breaker plate
4 screen pack
5 cartridge heater
6 insulation
7 electrical junction box

94

Fig. 2. Type DS screen changer for discontinuous operation.

Fig. 3. Type K-SWE-101 screen changer for continuous operation.

The pressure curve in fig. 4 shows the pressure profile for the various types.

Start of extrusion with clean screen	180 bar
Continuous rise until screen is changed, to	240 bar
Pressure difference	60 bar

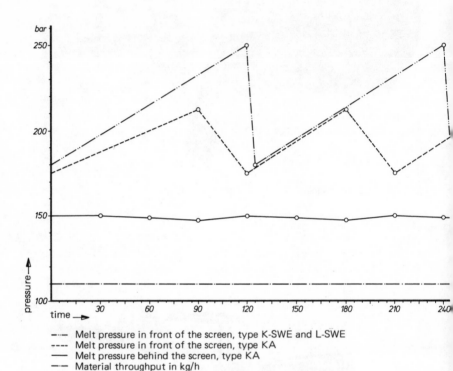

--·-- Melt pressure in front of the screen, type K-SWE and L-SWE
---- Melt pressure in front of the screen, type KA
—— Melt pressure behind the screen, type KA
--·- Material throughput in kg/h

Fig. 4. Pressure curves.

To balance out this pressure difference, there are continuous screen changers on the market now, which are controlled via the extrusion pressure, i. e. the fresh screen area exposed to the melt stream is such that the pressure increases only within the range of permissible product tolerance. This pressure can be set as required by the polymer and the end product. It should, however, be mentioned that such screen changers are suitable only for certain types of polymers.

96

c) Screen changers for continuous, automatic operation, i. e. production is not affected by changing the screen, taking place automatically via the set pressure.

Type KA

Constructional features

The most important characteristic of all the screen changers described below is that the screen is accomodated inside a cyclindrical sleeve henceforth to be referred to as a screen bushing [2]. This accomodates the exchangeable breaker plate with the screen and is moved inside the housing – normally hydraulically. The unit can also be designed with a spindle with hand wheel operation and possibly a pneumatic system for small extrusion lines, and is an inexpensive alternative among discontinuous equipment.

An important factor of this type of construction is that the seal in relation to the melt stream is produced solely via the tolerance between screen bushing and screen changer housing, as well as a sufficiently large surface area. No sealing elements which might wear out are incorporated, so that the screen changers will remain tight even after many years of use.

Design is for extrusion pressures up to 600 bar and thus greatly exceeds the extruder capacity. The melt viscosity determines the tolerance, which can amount to between 0.03 and 0.12 mm, depending on the screen changer size.

Screen changer housings and screen bushings are produced by a number of operations and their respective surface finishes must meet very exacting requirements. The melt flow zone are made without sharp transitions and their surfaces are polished. The surfaces of the screen changer and the screen bushing are then nitrided and this, coupled with the grade of steel used, produces an extremly hard surface which guarantees a perfect seal even at very high temperatures.

The system comprising screen bush and bore is easy to control from the machining point of view and inexpensive. The tolerances required for a particular polymer must be ascertained by the manufacturer in special tests.

The standard design for types K-SWE (i. e. screen changer for continuous operation) shown in fig. 5 is constructed so that the melt stream is passed from the extruder via an adapter, two flow-ways, the screens and another adapter, to the die. In other words, the melt stream is passed through two separate flow-ways between the melt entry side and melt exit side of the

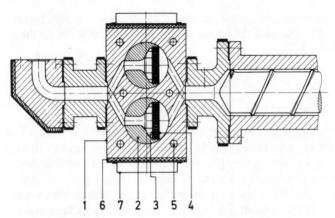

Fig. 5. Type K-SWE screen changer for continuous operation.

1   screen changer housing   5   cartridge heater
2   screen bush   6   insulation
3   breaker plate   7   electrical junction box
4   screen pack

screen changer, each flow-way being fitted with an exchangeable screen. During production, both screens are in use and only whilst a screen is being changed is a screen inside the screen bush moved out hydraulically. The melt stream is thus effectively blocked and is passed through the second screen bush whilst the first is being changed.

Thanks to the cross-sectional area of the housing and screen bush, including the breaker plate inside the bush, the increase in pressure during this phase is kept within limits. In the case of standard polymers and the already described pressure difference between spent and clean screens of around 50 bar, screens can thus be changed continuously without exceeding product tolerances.

The filtration device in the series KS [3] for continuous production, consists of a housing and several screen bushes arranged at right angles to the direction of polymer flow and connected positively with each other. When the screen has to be changed, the filtration chamber is deaerated, flooded with polymer melt and then moved into production position in less than 1 second by means of an hydraulic accumulator unit.

Another special feature is the breaker plates inside the screen bush. The free cross-section in these plates amounts to about 50 % of the total screen diameter and is therefore at a maximum, as shown in fig. 6. To enable the

98

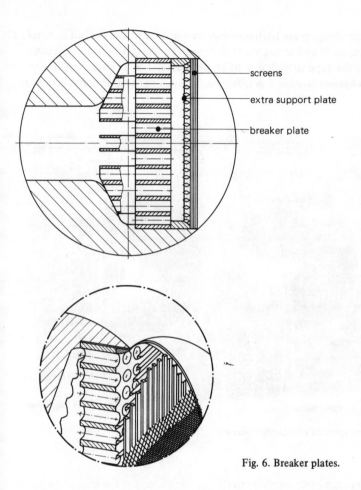

screens

extra support plate

breaker plate

Fig. 6. Breaker plates.

screen to be used fully, i. e. that the screen does not only strain off contaminant particles near the free area in the breaker plate, a special support plate is placed in front of the breaker plate, whose surface consists only of strips so that about 98 % of its surface is free. These plates are recommended for polymers with poor flow on account of their viscosity. In the case of nylon or polyester a sufficiently coarse screen support fulfills the same purpose.

The screen bushes have grooves of different lengths on the melt entry and exit sides, called vent grooves. Their function is important for continuous production and will be described later [2].

The screen changers are heated mainly by cartridge heaters. Their number, heating capacity and arrangement in the screen changer housing is dependent upon the type of polymer to be processed. The arrangement of the cartridge heaters is made specially clear in fig. 7. The cable connections are

Fig. 7. Arrangement of cartridge heaters.

passed through cable conduits to the junction boxes at the side of the housing. The connections can also be passed to plugs to facilitate quick dismantling of the extrusion line. The voltage of the cartridge heaters is normally 220 volts, but models with up to 500 volts can be supplied. The heating-up time of the screen changer is matched to the whole extrusion line and is about one hour. The maximum temperature is about 350 °C and is controlled via one or two heating sections. Thermocouple wells are situated at points where they are most convenient in relation to the melt stream.

The various screen changers on the market can be fitted to any make of extruder using two adaptors which are individually matched to the extruder and die.

100

Principle of operation

Screen changing is dependent upon the materials being processed, as well as on the production process. To make the fullest use of the screens, the maximum possible pressure increase is utilised. The pressure gauge should be incorporated in the adapter between the extruder and screen changer. In the case of the unit for discontinuous operation, the plant must be switched off so that the spent screen can be removed by means of an hydraulic cyclinder, hand wheel or pneumatic cylinder, and replaced by a fresh one. As soon as the clean screen is in position, the plant can be re-started.

Changing screens takes about 3 minutes but in the case of screen changers with two screen bores arranged in series only about one minute since the new screen can already be prepared for changing.

In the model K-SWE, screen changing is accomplished by means of the hydraulic unit and the hydraulic control valve assigned to each screen bush. The speed with which the screen bush moves depends on the hydraulic unit and is usually about 400 – 500 mm/min. Fig. 8 shows that the reason for the relatively slow movement of this screen bush is that, after exchanging the spent screen against a fresh one, the bush is moved into a so-called vent position to force out the air that has been introduced into the housing during the screen change. Evacuation of the filter chamber is essential during continuous production since the air that would otherwise be entrapped would cause a break in production and this is something that must be avoided at all costs, e. g. in the production of blown film, tearing of the film bubble would cause considerable waste of time and production losses. The vent position is limited by a stop and a small amount of melt is removed, via the vent grooves, to flood the space in front of the screen. The vent grooves are situated at the highest point so as to ensure that all the air is effectively removed.

A notable feature of this venting system is that the space in front of as well as behind the screen, i. e. the complete screen bush, can be deaerated without coming into contact with the melt stream. Only after complete deaeration can the screen bush be moved into the production position and the completed screen change be assessed with the help of the now evident pressure decrease. The other screen can be changed immediately afterwards or at a later stage, depending on the type of production process.

The screen bushes should be cleaned after dismantling, using the appropriate tools, so that there is no build-up of material and the unit can continue to function properly. The screen bushes are sprayed with a dry lubricant, based

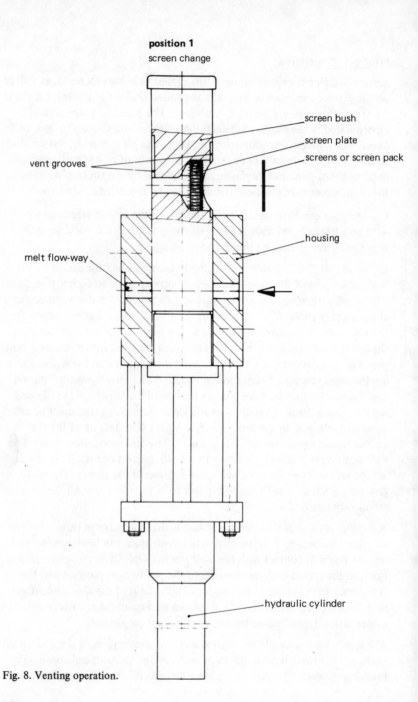

Fig. 8. Venting operation.

position 2
venting -
flooding on screen side

position 3
venting -
flooding on rear side

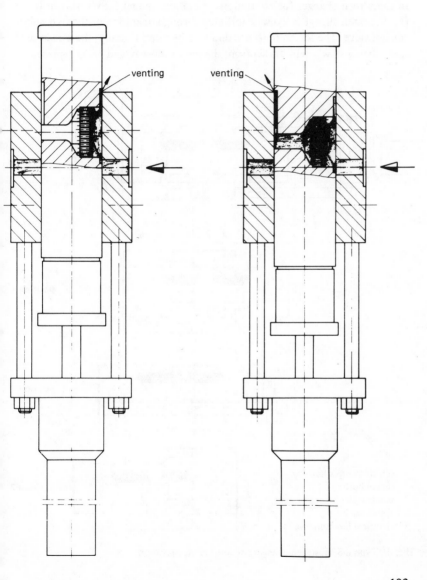

venting

venting

103

on molybdenum, at lengthy intervals. Lubricants based on natural products or silicones cannot be used since the former cannot stand up to the continuous high temperatures whilst the latter act as release agents which would cause blocking up at such small tolerances.

In the screen changer for continuous operation, model L-SWE shown in fig. 9, screen change is likewise initiated through operation of the hydraulic control valve. The screen bush continues to be moved axially, the screen surface 1 being slowly withdrawn from the melt flow-way and being replaced

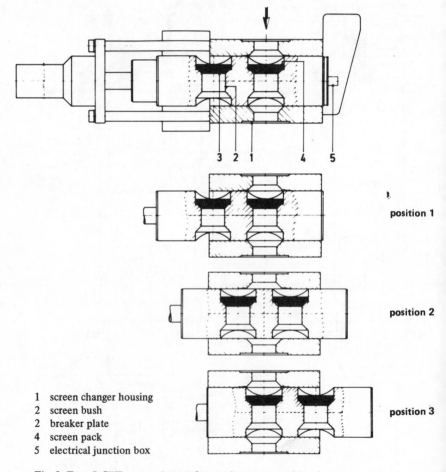

position 1

position 2

1   screen changer housing
2   screen bush
2   breaker plate
4   screen pack
5   electrical junction box

position 3

Fig. 9. Type L-SWE screen changer for continuous operation.

by screen surface 2. During this operation, melt already flows through a slit in the housing on to screen surface 2, displaces the air there, and, when the screen chamber 2 is completely full, flows into the open at the end of the housing. This indicates that the pre-flooding operation has been completed and that screen surface 2 can finally be aligned with the melt flow-way. The spent screen pack 1 can now be exchanged on the exposed breaker plate [4]. Changing screens takes about 2 − 3 minutes for model K-SWE as well as L-SWE.

In the screen changer type KA, for automatic operation, fig. 10, a constant pressure of the melt stream at the die is guaranteed during the filtration process. In this screen changer, a number of screen bush segments, arranged in a housing, are positively connected with each other [3]. Each segment hat three holes into each of which a circular screen pack is inserted.

The entire screen bush is hydraulically moved through the melt stream in adjustable steps, the number of stages and their duration being individually adjustable according to requirements and the degree of contamination. Auto-

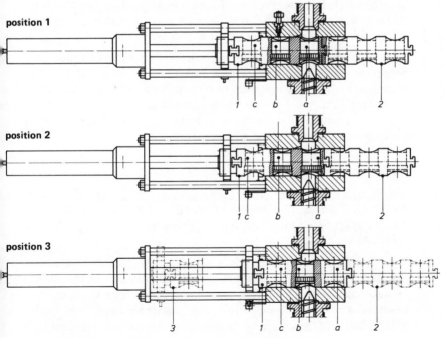

Fig. 10. Type KA screen changer for continuous operation.

105

matic operation is achieved with the help of pressure gauges in front of and behind the screen changer. Sporadic, increased contamination is recorded by special cycle devices and cause the rate of advance to be increased. In order to achieve continuous production, the housing contains a bypass for flooding or deaerating the next clean filter screen. Deaeration takes place via an adjustable valve, so that it is possible to deal with different melt viscosities.

Position 1 is the actual production position. Screen bush 1 with screen opening a in production, screen opening b in the pre-heating position.

Position 2 is the venting position, i. e. screen bush 1 with screen opening a in production, screen opening b is vented.

Position 3 shows the change position with screen bush 1 and screen opening b in production, screen opening c in the pre-heating position, screen bush 3 is placed in position with the connecting piece retracted, screen bush 2 is removed and cleaned.

An important feature of this design is that the heaters bring the new screen to the same temperature as the melt stream, this screen being flooded only immediately before use. Because of the venting operation, the complete screen bush segment must be taken out after it has reached its final position, and replaced as a clean element on the hydraulic side.

Such screen changers are used, for example, for blown film extrusion lines with screw diameters of up to 90 mm, using up to 100 % regrind. Uninterrupted blown film production can be achieved with such units, even when using regrind composed of materials of different densities and physical form, e. g. ground material, small pieces or agglomerates, if the process is properly controlled and the plant designed accordingly.

Circular filter screen gauzes

The fineness of the screen gauzes used is governed by the type of melts they are intended to filter. One can say, in general, that the screen should be coarse enough to last for as long as possible and fine enough to produce the required melt quality.

The screens used consist of cleanly punched, circular gauzes whose outside diameter is about 0.3 mm bigger than the inside diameter of the screen bushes. This prevents the screen becoming detached from the bush after insertion. A coarser mesh supporting gauze is placed in front of the breaker plate, followed, downstream, by the production screen either with a medium -mesh screen and a further supporting screen, or only with a production screen and supporting screen. The arrangement of the screen packs and their mesh size depends on the type of polymer to be processed, and its degree of contamination, the latter being determined by a number of methods using a laboratory extruder [5].

It should be remembered that the required back pressure can often be built up with the appropriate screen pack and that such screen packs improve melt homogeneity. The screen pack can consist of loose, individual gauzes, a spot-welded screen assembly or an enclosed combination of screen gauzes.

Special properties

Screen changers with slot seals can also be used in the processing of speciality polymers if certain components are suitable modified. In the processing of PMMA for example, a special flow section is incorporated into the K-SWE model to compensate for the extreme changes in cross-section found here. This facilitates optimum flow of the melt on to the screen and prevents the polymer from being affected by varying temperatures.

Reinforced hydraulic units, harder surface and increased heating capacity, coupled with the observance of prescribed tolerances between screen bush and screen changer housing enable difficult materials like nylon, polycarbonate and cellulose acetate to be processed without difficulty.

Technical data

The choice of screen changing unit for a given extruder size and throughput essentially depends on whether it is proposed to use virgin polymer mixed with regrind, or solely regrind. The following tables, figs. 11 and 12, are based on experience but it should be noted that the screen diameter should be roughly the same as the extruder screw diameter. The lower figures given in the tables apply to throughputs when using regrind, the higher ones to the throughputs achieved with virgin material. The screen changer can also be oversize, depending, on the type of polymer, so as to make the screen last a long time. Generally speaking however, it should be remembered that too small a screen diameter will result in unwanted pressure build-up and reduction of the extruder's capacity.

Because of the circular screen bush system and the described slot seal, the maximum screen diameter is 270 mm. The throughput of 4.5 tonnes/h does, however, require the use of an extruder equipped with a 250 or 300 mm screw, see fig. 13.

107

model	for extruder throughput in kg/h	screen area		220 Volt cartridge heaters		housing dimensions		
		cm²	φ mm	number	Watt	a	b	c
K-SWE- 50	~ 40	2 x 17	46.3	4	630	120	190	230
K-SWE- 80	40− 150	2 x 27	58.3	4	1000	180	300	230
K-SWE-100	80− 230	2 x 45	76.3	4	1000	180	300	230
K-SWE-101	140− 300	2 x 70	96.3	4	1000	180	300	230
K-SWE-121	200− 420	2 x 105	116.3	4	1000	220	360	310
K-SWE-150	350− 780	2 x 154	140.3	8	1000	280	420	440
K-SWE-160	520− 860	2 x 175	148.3	8	1000	280	420	440
K-SWE-180	700−1150	2 x 245	176.3	12	1000	350	500	440
K-SWE-250	1000−1800	2 x 415	230.3	16	1000	450	660	540
K-SWE-280	2400−3200	2 x 490	250	24	1250	500	760	600
K-SWE-300	4500	2 x 572	270	24	1250	540	800	640

Fig. 11. Technical data for type K-SWE screen changers.

model	extruder throughput kg/h*	screen		cartridge heaters		housing
		cm²	φ mm	number	W/piece	a x b x c (mm)
D-SWE- 62	40− 70	26	58,3	2	1000	140 x 140 x 220
D-SWE- 80	70−120	45	76,3	2	1000	160 x 160 x 240
D-SWE-100	110−180	72	96,3	4	1000	180 x 180 x 260
D-SWE-120	160−260	105	116,3	4	1000	200 x 200 x 280
D-SWE-144	230−390	154	140,3	4	1000	220 x 220 x 320
D-SWE-152	260−430	172	148,3	4	1000	230 x 230 x 330
D-SWE-180	370−610	244	176,3	4	1000	260 x 260 x 360

Fig. 12. Technical data for type D-SWE screen changers.

108

weight kg	height mm	connecting dimensions in mm				electrical connection hydraulics
		A	B	C	D	
70	600	35	50	100	8 x M12, 20 deep	
175	850	50	80	140	8 x M16, 25 deep	
175	850	50	80	140	8 x M20, 25 deep	
180	850	50	80	140	8 x M20, 25 deep	
310	930	45	80	160	8 x M20, 25 deep	
675	1150	65	100	190	8 x M20, 25 deep	220/380 Volt
680	1150	65	100	190	8 x M20, 25 deep	
910	1200	90	130	200	8 x M20, 25 deep	
2060	1560	150	200	320	8 x M30, 25 deep	
2760	1700	170	220	400	8 x M30, 35 deep	
3180	1750	170	220	400	8 x M30, 35 deep	

weight kg	height h	stroke H	connecting dimensions				electrical connection Volt
			A	B	C	D	
62	425	140	20	40	110 x 4	M20, 25 deep	
76	655	160	30	50	120 x 6	M20, 25 deep	
103	825	180	50	70	110 x 8	M20, 25 deep	
115	855	200	50	70	150 x 8	M20, 25 deep	220
174	895	230	50	70	150 x 8	M20, 25 deep	
189	910	240	60	80	170 x 8	M20, 25 deep	
242	1020	270	70	90	170 x 8	M20, 25 deep	

Fig. 13. Type K-SWE 280 screen changer with base.

Applications

Whereas the first screen changers were used only for scrap granulation, they are becoming necessary in every production plant. Fitting such screen changers to existing extruders is no problem, whatever their make, using appropriately designed adaptors, see fig. 14.

In the production of polymers, screen changers are normally used only where worthwhile improvements can be achieved thereby. It must be remembered that, for example in the pelletisation of nylon or polycarbonates, it is primarily gel particles which must be eliminated, besides small amounts of solid contaminants. Only very rarely will such gel particles make it possible to use a screen to its full capacity since even with slight rise in pressure they will slip through the finest mesh screen, making frequent screen changes necessary.

Other applications for screen changers are:
— blown film extrusion
— flat film extrusion

110

- chill-roll equipment
- sheet extrusion
- profile extrusion
- blow moulding machines
- film tape extruders
- filament extrusion
- co-extrusion
- recycling equipment (especially important).

Economic considerations

There are various possibilities for the economic use of the different kinds of screen changer. In view of the quality of present-day virgin moulding compounds, a discontinuous screen changer will be quite sufficient e. g. for blown film extrusion. Since the life of a correctly chosen screen will exceed the life of the whole extrusion line. This means that interruptions due to the production process such as cleaning the blown film die or checks on other parts of the equipment, can be utilised to change the screen. The increasing use of regrind material, especially in blown film extrusion, should however be taken into account already when the plant is being designed since frequent screen changes require the use of screen changers to achieve continuous production.

Screen changers in fibre and spinning equipment enable already incorporated screen packs in the dies to be better utilised. Screen changers for continuous operation can pre-filter the polymer melt since, at this point, screens can be changed at any time without interrupting production. Changing the screen packs in the dies can therefore be greatly delayed and the downtime reduced.

There are various ways in which screen changers can be used [6]. On the assumption that thermoplastic melts have to be filtered and cleaned, it is necessary to relate the resultant cost to the various kinds of operating conditions as well as to the fact that a wide range of different polymers has to be processed. This is why it is not possible to provide generally applicable information on the type and size of equipment. In order to obtain a general impression of how economical screen changers are, reference must be made to standard plastics processing equipment.

The advantage of a screen changer for continuous operation in a recycling plant for example is easily demonstrated since the use of a built-in breaker plate with screen pack is quite uneconomical and therefore out of the question. Screen changers for discontinuous operation must be rejected for the same reasons since even short interruptions in a die-face pelletiser are very expensive.

Summarising, we can say that screen changers not only improve end product quality but are economical, so that the initial outlay is soon recovered. The consumption of screens must be considered in much the same light. Where screens are not changed frequently, where screen packs or spot-welded screens are used, these are destroyed when they have become dirty. If more screens are needed and, especially when using coarse-mesh screens, they can now be cleaned and re-used.

Maximum utilisation of the screens, recognisable by the rise in extrusion pressure, inevitably means reduced extruder efficiency. In certain applications, e. g. the production of PP filament tape, blown film production etc., this reduced efficiency is compensated as far as possible by increasing screw speed or altering the take-off speed. By making use of the maximum possible pressure increase, best use will also be made of the whole extrusion line. Apart from recycling plants, production losses are negligible.

Method of operation

Operation of screen changers, with their connection to an hydraulic unit, hydraulic cylinder and control valve are easy to operate. The venting and flooding process for the new screen pack is made clearly visible by optical and mechanical means and requires but little practice on the part of operators provided a pressure gauge is available. Venting must be done with special care in those areas where narrow production tolerances are required because the pressure differences between dirty and clean screens are only slight.

Bibliography

[1] BASF: Kunststoff-Physik im Gespräch. 1977.
[2] Westhoff: DBP 18 00 1669 (1968).
[3] *Kreyenborg, J.:* DBP 22 56 639 (1972).
[4] *Tenner, H.:* Aufbereiten von Kunststoffabfällen. VDI-Verlag GmbH, Düsseldorf 1973.
[5] *Herrmann, Ch.:* Aufbereiten von Kunststoffabfällen. VDI-Verlag GmbH, Düsseldorf 1973.
[6] *Kreyenborg, U.:* Kunststofftechnik No. 5 (1974).

Cassette systems with and without pre-filling

Albert Herbener

Design requirements

a) Simple, trouble-free and easy-to-service construction of the screen changer.

b) The tolerance fields of th elements to be made should be such that they can be mass produced and easily exchanged.

c) Smooth operation at different temperatures, pressures and viscosities.

d) Easy dismantling of screen cassettes without having to use tools, for subsequent cleaning.

e) Screen cassettes should move in only one direction, i. e. when they are pushed in and subsequently changed, so as to prevent dirt or charred polymer reaching the melt stream.

f) Uninterrupted production even during screen changing.

Constructional features

Cassette screen changers are normally constructed with a screw thread, as can be seen from fig. 1.

The model shown in fig. 1 is equipped with an additional clamping frame so as to prevent the polymer melt penetrating between the cassettes whilst the screen is being changed.

The right-angled slit in the screen changer housing is formed by two strips (1) and the two halves of the housing (28) and (29). The whole assembly is tightened by the screws (25). The cassettes (32) can be moved in the rectangular slit with the hydraulic cylinder (26). To avoid tolerance accumulations, additional wear plates are avoided as far as possible, i. e. the housing halves (28) and (29) must be made of tempered steel and have wear resistant sliding surfaces.

Fig. 2 shows a cassette screen changer for relatively stable polymers such as polyethylene, polystyrene, polypropylene etc. This design is equipped with

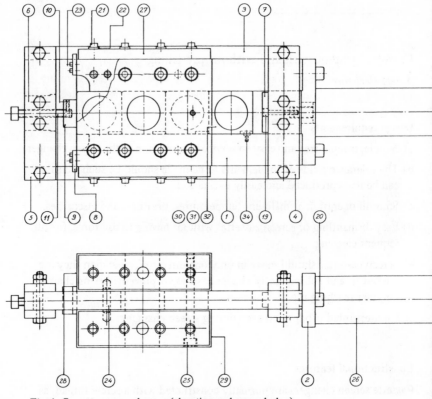

Fig. 1. Cassette screen changer (elevation and ground plan).

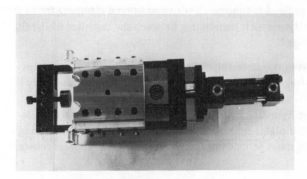

Fig. 2. Cassette screen changer with clamping frame and pre-filling system for PE, PP etc.

114

clamping frames for the cassettes and a pre-filling device for continuous production.

Fig. 3 shows a cassette screen changer for PVC or rubber with an extraction device for the screen cassette in the sealing position. The melt inside the cassette would otherwise degrade or harden in the sealing position, resulting in the entire screen changing system becoming clogged. Pre-filling is not possible with this type of screen changer.

Fig. 3. Cassette screen changer with extraction device for PVC and rubber.

Fig. 4. Screen cassettes.

Fig. 4 shows a screen cassette and a cassette with a through-hole. These cassettes are made of a high chromium grade of steel and depth-hardened. The high chromium content protects against corrosion and increases the resistance of the cassettes to cleaning baths. The cassette surfaces must be precision ground so as to avoid damage during starting-up. Chemical attack on the steel can likewise be reduced by means of a high quality surface finish.

115

The steel used for screen changer housing, strips and cassettes is chosen so that the thermal expansion of these components at different extrusion temperatures remains as constant as possible. This also ensures that the clearance between the screen changer housing and the cassettes remains constant. It is, of course, the extent of this clearance which is directly responsible for the tightness of the screen changing system.

The screws which hold the screen changer housing together should always be tightened in several stages using the right torque wrench so that all the screws are uniformly loaded. The torque is fixed at about 80 % of the maximum permissible tensile stress of the screws. The resultant clamping force must be sufficient to withstand the maximum extrusion pressure.

Principle of operation

Fig. 5 shows the positions of the cassette system:

a) loading position
b) pre-heating position
c) filtering position
d) sealing position
e) discharging position
f) hydraulic cylinder
g) main melt stream
h) overflow

Screen cassette changing procedure

When a screen cassette has to be changed, a new one is moved into the loading position. The piston rod of the hydraulic cylinder f now moves all four screen cassettes a, b, c and d forward by one position, so that cassette a becomes b, b becomes c etc. The last cassette d is ejected from the screen changer housing and is caught by an appropriate receptacle, ready for cleaning.

The piston rod then moves backwards, freeing position a so that a new cassette can be moved into the loading position.

The screen cassette in pre-heating position b must remain in this position at least until it has reached the temperature of the screen changer housing, which takes about 15 minutes. If changing is done more quickly, the cassette does not have sufficient time to expand to the final thickness, so that

116

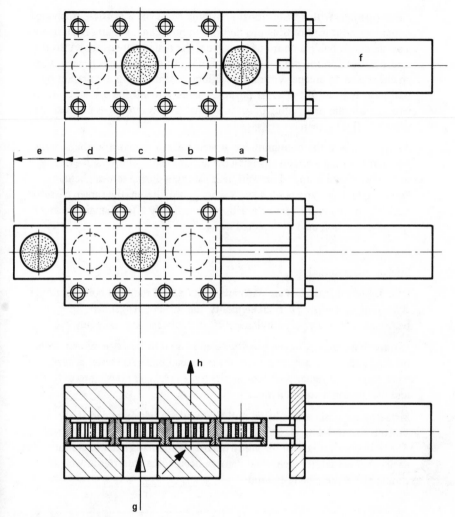

Fig. 5. Operation of a cassette system.

there is a likelihood of polymer melt penetrating between the housing and cassette surfaces. The screen changer thus becomes leaky or the whole system becomes clogged.

It is possible, when using cassette screen changers, to keep the melt stream flowing even whilst the screen is being changed, since the screen inserts are close together. With an additional pre-filling device, it is possible to change screens without interrupting production. In pre-filling, the aim is to divert a small, controllable amount of melt from the main melt stream g into the screen cassette in the pre-heating position b. An overflow h is necessary to enable the air to escape. Various pre-filling systems are on the market but basically, they fulfil the same purpose, namely to fill the screen cassette with melt in the pre-heating position so that the product does not tear off when the filter screen is exchanged.

As fig. 5 shows, the contaminated screen cassette remains in the sealing position d during a screen changing cycle. This is difficult to solve in any other way if one wants to prevent melt escaping during screen changing. When unstable polymers such as PVC are being filtered, the screen cassette can be removed in the sealing position immediately after changing, using a special extraction device, depicted in fig. 3.

Special characteristics

Cassette screen changers are particularly suited for modular construction. By adding or omitting certain elements, the screen changer can, for example, be used for filtering polyethylene, PVC or rubber mixes, as required.

Differently designed screen cassettes can be used in the same screen changer housing and it is relatively easy to make special screen cassettes according to customers' requirements. Adapting the screen changer housing to extruders and dies presents no problems.

Maintenance costs are reduced and the working life extended if the non-ferrous metal sliding plates are replaced by those made of nitrided steel. The only disadvantage of having two hard components in close contact with each other is that, if mechanical damage occurs, the cassettes as well as the sliding plates must be re-ground.

Technical data

Cassette screen changers are at present being made for filter screen diameters of 30 − 250 mm. The larger ones are a little difficult to handle and it is often necessary to resort to a loading and transport device for the cassettes.

The maximum pressure which cassette screen changers will withstand is solely a matter of the design of the screws which hold the housing together, and the thickness of the housing blocks. There are cassette screen changers on the market which are used with maximum extrusion pressures of 800 bar. Normal maximum pressures are 500 bar.

Typical applications

For relatively stable polymers such as polyethylene, polystyrene, polypropylene etc., one uses pre-filling, which we have already discussed. The resultant advantage, not to run the risk of the product tearing off during screen changing, is particularly evident where "threading" a torn-off product back into the machine is time consuming and costly, e. g. blown and cast film, pipe, profile, sheet and strand pelletising applications.

A second important consideration is that every time a filter screen is changed, a cassette is automatically expelled from the housing and can immediately pass to the cleaning station. No extra equipment is thus needed for removing the screen cassettes.

In the case of unstable polymers such as PVC, or vulcanising rubber, the pre-filling system cannot be used since the melt would char or cure in the overflow channel. In such cases, the air inside the screen cassette in the pre-heating position is removed by means of a vacuum pump or a venturi nozzle. By synchronising the haul-off device at the end of the extrusion line with the screen changer advance, it is possible, here too, to largely prevent the product from breaking off.

Economic aspects

The most important factors influencing profitability calculations for a screen changer are investment costs, depreciation, overall maintenance costs, labour savings and increased efficiency of the extrusion plant. In most cases, these factors can be determined only by the extruder company itself.

Nowadays, screen changing units are already fitted to new extruders by the manufacturers. It is nevertheless important to equip existing extruders with screen changers.

The great economic advantage of cassette screen changers is that they are hardly likely to break down, as well as the possibility of maintaining continuous production. Technical assistance when fitting a screen changer to an extruder by the screen changer manufacturer can save the customer much time and wory and has a direct effect on the economic efficiency of the screen changing system.

Large area, twin-chamber filter with change-over device for use in continuous extrusion

Friedhelm Hensen

Increasing production speeds make considerable demands on the purity of polymer melts. Especially when stretching filaments or thin film, solid particles in the melt must not be bigger than a fraction of the filament diameter or the film thickness because bigger particles would cause the filament or film to tear during stretching. The same happens if the melt contains particles having a degree of polymerisation greatly different from that of the base polymer.

During the development and use of filtration units, it was found that foreign particles or unmelted polymer particles which would interfere with stretching, could be removed by means of filtration provided one uses a screen with a small enough mesh size or a fine-pore filter medium, and that the melt flow rate is extremely slow and the pressure gradient on both sides of the filter extremely small.

Demands made on a melt filtration unit

A filter placed between the extruder barrel and the die should increase energy consumption only within certain permissible limits (fig. 1). The above mentioned conditions can therefore be met only if the melt stream is distributed across a very large surface area and brought together again. This requirement led to the development of large area filters. Another requirement is that the product to be filtered should pass through the filter as quickly as possible and this is why a maximum effective filtration area should be accomodated in a minimum of space. This can be achieved by accomodating the filters in filtration chambers, the filtration media being clamped in candle-shaped, hollow bodies (fig. 2) or being pressed into hollow, discus-shaped objects from sintered powder (fig. 3). The ratio of filter area F to chamber volume V should be greater than $100 \text{ m}^2/\text{m}^3$. In the designs described below it is $250 - 300 \text{ m}^2/\text{m}^3$.

Other conditions filters must fulfil are:

They should be easy to install.

They must be easy to clean.

121

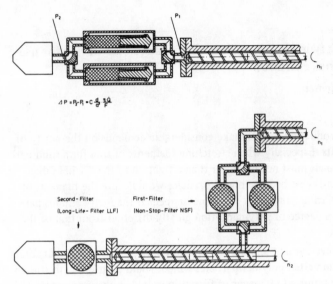

Fig. 1. Arrangement of large area filter in the extrusion plant and pressure gradient Δp.

$P_1 P_2$ = melt pressure in front of and behind the melt filter
C = constant
d = wire diameter
η = viscosity
$\dot{Q}$ = throughput
a = mesh size
F = filter area

It should be possible to fit them without interrupting the extrusion process.

The filter housing should be heatable.

The filter medium should be easily exchanged.

Design features of large area filters

The above mentioned demands are met if two filter chambers are arranged parallel to each other, as shown in fig. 4. These chambers are designed as cylindrical inserts (fig. 5) in which the filter medium – in the form of candles or hollow discs – acts as a separating wall between the melt inlet in the cover and melt outlet in the base (fig. 6). The filter inserts are accomodated in two heated, cyclindrical housings equipped with seals against the melt on the valve side and, opposite these, tightening screws. The filter housings are

122

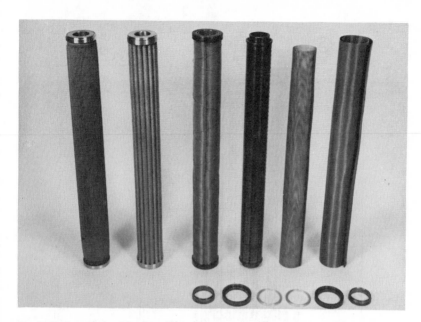

Fig. 2. Various kinds of filter candles.

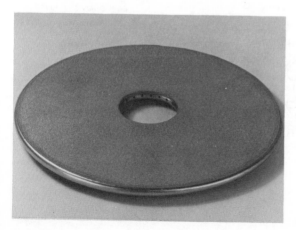

Fig. 3. Discus insert.

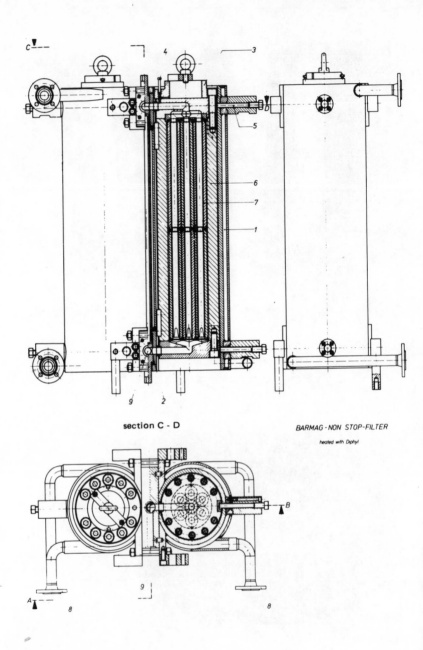

section C - D

BARMAG - NON STOP-FILTER

heated with Diphyl

Fig. 4. Non-stop large area filter.

124

Fig. 5. Large area filter with filter insert having an area of 46.5 m².

125

Fig. 6. Dismantled filter insert with a filter area of 3.5 m².

linked by three-way to enable the melt to flow in and out. These taps also serve as a means of changing over the melt stream to a clean filter when one filter has to be changed.

Principle of operation and operating details

As fig. 7 shows, the valves are operated via spindles and handwheel. The spindles are connected by a sprocket chain drive. The valves can be changed over separately or together by means of couplings.

Fig. 8 shows the operating principle with reference to the valve position and pressure profile in front of and behind the filter during the change-over process when the filter is being changed. Here, one can see from left to right how the melt pressure in front of the filter increases due to the filter medium becoming dirty, whilst behind the filter it is kept constant by controlling pressure and screw speed or by means of a metering pump. When the permissible

126

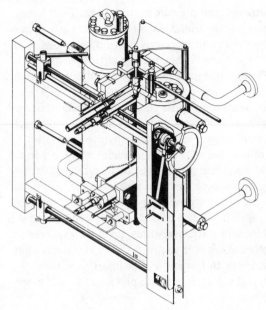

Fig. 7. Structure of large area filter with two filter housings.

maximum pressure is reached, the melt inlet valve is adjusted in such a way that some of the melt is diverted to flood the cleaned filter insert without interrupting the main stream.

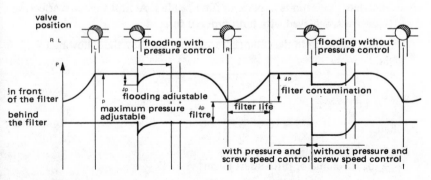

Fig. 8. Qualitative pressure-time diagram for filter life and filter change.

127

The reduced resistance causes the melt pressure in front of the filter to drop briefly. Simultaneously, the pressure behind the filter drops for as long as an amount of melt, reduced by the amount necessary for flooding, flows. The position of valve is limited by the permissible pressure reduction Δp for maintaining production. The required pressure behind the filter is re-instated by means of the pressure/screw speed controls. After flooding has been completed, the main melt stream resumes its course through the cleaned filter insert. Both valves are completely switched over, causing the melt pressure in front of the filter to drop to the level dictated by the filter resistance Δp. Contamination of the cleaned filter insert causes a renewed rise in pressure until the permitted maximum pressure has been reached in front of the filter. The same change-over process then takes place. In the right hand part of the diagram we see the pressure profile for a plant without pressure/screw speed controls. The pressure increase caused by filter contamination is permitted to be up to 150 bar and is attained within 1 − 3 weeks, depending on the purity of the melt and the pore size of the filter medium. Filters connected in series can last for up to 12 months. The insert to be flooded is filled with an inert gas before flooding, in order to prevent melt oxidation and hydrolytic decomposition.

To achieve a sensibly sized filter surface for present-day filtration problems, a standard filter candle, 500 mm long and 60 mm in diameter was chosen, which produces a surface area of 0.1 m² if the filter medium is smooth and 0.5 m² if it is fluted.

The candles can be arranged as shown in fig. 9, with different lengths and cross-sections, so that up to 93 filter candles form a unit. Discus-shaped units are also available in standard sizes. The measurements of the filter housings were chosen so that in the case of certain sizes, it is possible to accomodate discus units in place of filter candles. Almost the same effective filter area was achieved with both types of filter.

The residence time in the filter (in seconds) is given by the following formula:

$$L = \frac{V}{\dot{Q}}$$

where

L = residence time

V = melt volume of filter insert in cm^3

$\dot{Q}$ = melt throughput in cm^3/s

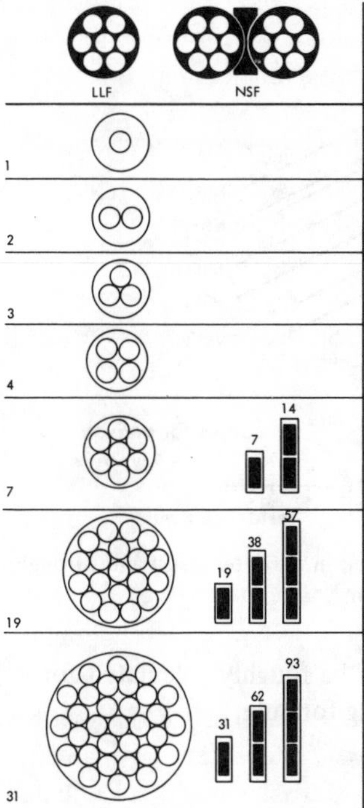

	Filter type		Number of cartridges	
	NSF	LLF	NSF	LLF
1	1		2 × 1	1 × 1
2	2		2 × 2	1 × 2
3	3		2 × 3	1 × 3
4	4		2 × 4	1 × 4
7	7		2 × 7	1 × 7
	14		2 × 14	1 × 14
19	19		2 × 19	1 × 19
	38		2 × 38	1 × 38
	57		2 × 57	1 × 57
31	31		2 × 31	1 × 31
	62		2 × 62	1 × 62
	93		2 × 93	1 × 93

Fig. 9. Range of large area filters with filter candles and discus units.

If the melt throughput is given as weight per unit time, it is necessary to take the specific weight into account. Fig. 10 shows the relationship between residence time of the screw in the filter and throughput for various filter sizes in the range. The graph shows that the residence time is only a few minutes even with the filter NSF 93, the biggest filter made so far, with 93 filter candles equivalent to an effective filter area of 46.5 m^2, the melt throughput being sufficient. A uniform residence time for all separate melt streams is achieved by making the melt flow-ways the same length — also inside the valves — and by rheologically favourable design of the housing and filter candles or discus units.

In deciding on the filter size, filter resistance must be considered as well as residence time. Filter resistance is characterised by the pressure loss Δp

129

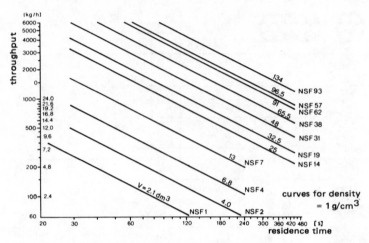

Fig. 10. Relationship between residence time of melt in the filter insert and throughput for different filter sizes and a melt density of 1 g/cm³.

between filter inlet and outlet, and this can be roughly calculated for a uniform wire mesh according to the following formula:

$$\Delta p = p_2 - p_1 = C \times \frac{d \, \eta \, \dot{Q}}{a^2 \, F} \quad (dyne/cm^2)$$

where

d = wire diameter in cm

η = melt viscosity in mPa.s

$\dot{Q}$ = melt throughput in cm³/s

a = mesh width in μm

F = filter area in m²

C = constant

Porous films or thin-walled housings made of sintered metal powder or sintered metal fibre webs may also be used. No definite mesh or pore sizes are given for these filter media, which makes it difficult to calculate the filter resistance. The pressure loss for these filter media is therefore calculated empirically. Fig. 11 shows figures actually measured for different filter cloths. If it is too difficult to measure the pressure gradient for a polymer melt, the pressure loss can be determined using a reference liquid such as silicone fluid and converted according to the following relationship:

130

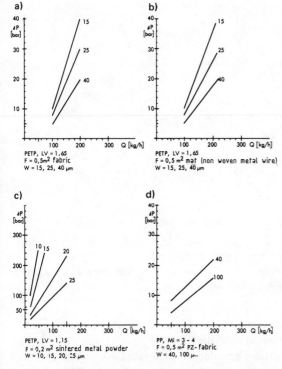

Fig. 11. Pressure loss of different filter media as a function of throughput for various polymers. The parameter is the mesh or pore size in μm.

a: PETP with solution viscosity* 1.65, filter area 0.5 m², woven wire mesh
b: PETP with solution viscosity* 1.65, filter area 0.5 m², non woven mat
c: PETP with solution viscosity* 1.65, filter area 0.2 m², sintered metal powder
d: PP with melt flow index (at 230 °C and 2.16 kg in g/10 min) of 3, filter area 0.5 m², PZ fabric
* Solution viscosity was measured in m-cresol.

$$\Delta p = \Delta p_{ref.} \times \frac{\eta_s}{\eta_{ref.}}$$

where

$\Delta p_{ref.}$ = pressure loss when using reference liquid

η_s = melt viscosity

$\eta_{ref.}$ = viscosity of reference liquid

131

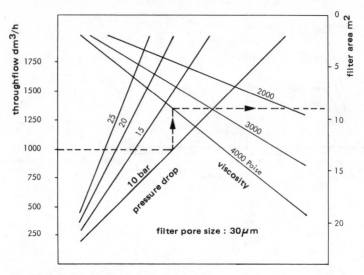

Fig. 12. Relationship between melt throughput, melt viscosity, pressure loss and filter area at a pore size of 30 μm.

From the empirically determined values one can produce a nomogram to help in the design and selection of the filter area, as shown in fig. 12. The example shows, with arrows, how one can ascertain the required filter area, starting out from the plant's melt throughput via the selected initial pressure drop and the given melt viscosity. This filter area is achieved by varying the number of filter candles or discus units, as shown in fig. 9, remembering the standard measurements of $0.1 - 0.5$ m^2 per filter candle.

During use, the filter resistance increases due to the filter becoming clogged. In practice, a pressure difference of 100 bar has proved to be in order. At higher melt pressures, too many dirt particles can be forced through the filter, either through being compressed or through widening of the mesh.

There comes a point when both the filter housing and filter inserts have to be cleaned. Filter housings can be cleaned with solvent, fluid bath, by pyrolysis or heating in an oven at 450 °C or in a salt bath also at 450 °C. Cleaning the filter inserts is far more difficult, depending on the plastic, e. g. by calcining in an inert gas atmosphere or in vacuo, or, for example in the case of PETP filter inserts, by rinsing with glycol, followed by cleaning in an ultrasonic bath. Table 1 gives a comparison of the various methods of cleaning.

132

Table 1. Comparison of methods of cleaning melt filters.

Cleaning process	Wire mesh	Filter medium sintered metal powder	Sintered fibre web
Solvent	5	4	5
Fluid bath	4	3	5
Vacuum pyrolysis	4	3	4
Calcining in oven	2	3	1
Salt bath	3	3	1

Assessment: from 5 = preferred method to 1 = not recommended.

Properties of filter media

The various filter media differ not only in their mesh or pore size but, as can be seen from fig. 13, in their ability to separate small particles from the melt stream at the same average mesh or pore size. This characteristic can best be assessed by comparing porosity, capillary twist and thickness of the filter medium [3]. The porosity as a measure of permeability is given by

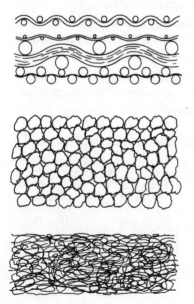

Fig. 13. Cross-sections of filter media.

$$s_p = 1 - \frac{m_{FM}}{\rho_{FM} \times V_{FM}}$$

where

s_p = porosity
m_{FM} = weight of filter medium
ρ_{FM} = density of filter medium
V_{FM} = volume of filter medium

Because of the structure of the filter medium, the partial flow channels are coiled or twisted. The capillary twisting w_i is another important characteristic of the filter medium besides porosity:

$$w_i = K \times \frac{l_f}{l_d}$$

where

K = constant
l_F = length of capillary
l_d = thickness of filter medium.

The capillary twist is always equal to or bigger than unity.

The word capillary is applied to the partial melt flow path inside the filter medium. The greater the capillary twist, the more twisted will be the melt flowpath and the greater will be the efficiency of the filtering medium.

Apart from the porosity and capillary twist the thickness of the medium is of importance, since this is proportional to the other filter characteristics and inversely proportional to the filter life.

Table 2. Normal values for porosity, capillary twist and thickness of different filter media.

Filter medium		Wire mesh	Sintered metal powder	Sintered metal fibres
Mesh size	μm	10 – 40	10 – 40	10 – 40
Porosity	μm	0.3 – 0.6	0.3 – 0.5	0.6 – 0.9
Capillary twist	μm	1.2 – 1.5	1.4 – 1.6	1.02 – 1.2
Thickness	mm	0.13 – 0.18	3.1 – 6.2	0.25 – 1

Table 2 gives normal values for porosity, capillary twist and thickness for various filter media. It is evident that sintered filter media are much thicker than comparable woven wire fabrics. These latter are normally made from wires whose diameters correspond to the mesh size, this resulting in thin products. Sintered metal powders are made as housings with a supporting function, necessitating thicker sections. The thickness of woven wire fabric and fibre mats can be increased by combining a number of layers.

Selection criteria

Besides the filter characteristics dictated by mesh size, porosity, capillary twist and thickness of the filter medium, economic efficiency and ease of cleaning are further factors which govern the selection of a filter medium. These can be assessed as shown in table 3.

Table 3. Assessment of selection criteria for filter media.

Filter medium	Wire mesh	Metal powder	Metal fibre mat
Filter properties	3	4	4
Reliability	4	5	4
Economic efficiency (life, cost, re-usuability)	4	2	3
Possibility of cleaning (solvent, calcining etc.)	4	3	2

Assessment: from 1 = unsuitable to 5 = highly suitable

Uses for large area filters

Large area filters offer major advantages if a particular process requires the melt to be specially clean, especially if the melt has to be oriented above the crystallite melting point or the semi-finished material below it. Fig. 14 shows the most important applications.

In polymer production, large area filters are used in order to improve the quality and processability of the granules, the surface area varying between 19 and 46.5 m² for melt throughputs of 3000 – 6000 kg/h. These size enable mesh sizes of 20 – 40 μm to be used, which will keep back most of the gel particles. If one judges the suitability of the resultant granular compound for the exacting process of high speed spinning of sythetic fibres, one finds

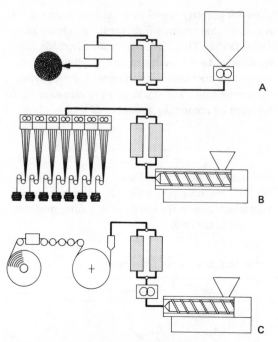

Fig. 14. Typical applications for large area filters.
A: polymer pelletisation, througphut 1000 – 10,000 kg/h
B: high speed spinning at speeds of up to 6000 m/min
C: production of biaxially oriented film, 2 – 2000 μm thick at 100 – 4,500 kg/h

that the use of these filters at the pelletising stage not only greatly improves spinning performance but also cuts down the amount of cleaning necessary by one-third.

Nowodays, large area filters are being used in nearly all continuous processing plants. Processing and quality improvements are particularly apparent in the production of synthetic filaments, fibres and non woven fabrics, as well as mono and biaxially oriented films, since great demands are made on polymer purity and homogeneity in view of the stresses to which the polymer is subjected during stretching, especially at high processing speeds.

In the production of synthetic filaments by spinneret extrusion, separate filters are normally used for each spinneret. By using a central filter, the life of the spinnerets is prolonged three to five-fold (fig. 15), the number of filament breaks also being greatly decreased.

136

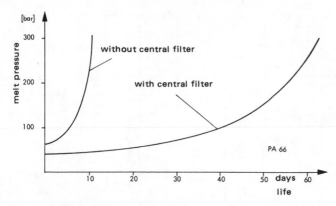

Fig. 15. Example of prolongation of spinneret life by using a central large area filter when processing nylon 66.

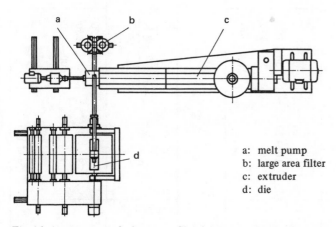

a: melt pump
b: large area filter
c: extruder
d: die

Fig. 16. Arrangement of a large area filter between melt metering pump and film die.

Table 4. Production data for various kinds of oriented film.

| Type of film | Dimensions of Oriented film | | Throughput (kg/h) |
	thickness (μm)	width (mm)	
Capacitor film	2 – 5	2000	300
Recording tape film	4 – 12	2800	400
Photographic film	100 – 300	4000	200 – 4500

137

Table 5. Summary of fields of use, mesh size and throughput for different filter sizes.

Field of application	filter area [m²] mesh size μm	0.1 – 0.5	0.4 – 2.0	0.7 – 3.5	1.4 – 7.0
		recommended throughput kg/h			
PETP-polycondensation	20 – 40	–	–	500 – 1000	1000 – 2000
PA-polymerisation	20 – 40	–	–	500 – 1000	1000 – 2000
PETP-stretched film production	10 – 20	30 – 60	100 – 300	200 – 500	400 – 1000
PETP- and PA spinning	20 – 30	50 – 150	100 – 300	400 – 700	600 – 1400
PP-stretched film production	40 – 80 and 150	100 – 300	100 – 2000	1500 – 3000	–

Field of application	filter area m² mesh size	1.9 – 9.5	3.8 – 19.0	5.7 – 28.5	9.3 – 46.5
		recommended throughput kg/h			
PETP-polycondensation	20 – 40	1500 – 2500	2000 – 4000	3000 – 6000	4000 – 10000
PA-polymerisation	20 – 40	1500 – 2500	2000 – 4000	3000 – 6000	4000 – 10000
PETP-stretched film production	10 – 20	600 – 1300	1000 – 3000	2000 – 4000	–
PETP- and PA spinning	20 – 30	–	–	–	–
PP-stretched film production	40 – 80 and 150	–	–	–	–

The quality improvement resulting from the use of large area filters is particularly evident in the case of biaxial stretching plants. Fig. 16 shows the position of the large area filter between melt pump and film die [4].

In the production of film used to make recording tape $4 - 12\ \mu m$ thick, capacitor films $2 - 5\ \mu m$ thick and transparent photosensitive films, the improvements in quality and economic performance also become apparent (table 4). These films could not be produced without the use of large area filters.

Here, the capacity of the extruder and downstream machines can be fully utilised so that throughputs of up to 4500 kg/h can be achieved.

Table 5 summarises the applications, mesh size and throughputs for different filter sizes.

Thanks to large area filters it is possible to process high proportions of regrind. The life of the filter will, of course, be shorter under these conditions, depending on the degree of contamination of the material.

In conclusion, it is clear that large area filtration has made a major contribution towards extrusion technology with regard to the economical use of raw materials, processing plants and end product properties and quality.

Bibliography

[1] *Hensen, F.* a. *E. Gathmann:* Kunststoffe 64, pp. 343/349, 1974.

[2] *Baker, J. W.:* Fiber Producer 80, pp. 22/26, april 1980.

[3] *Morland, C. D.* a. *B. Williams:* Fibre Producer 80, pp. 32/44 a. 65, april 1980.

[4] *Hensen, F.* a. *H. Bongaerts:* Plastverarbeiter 30, pp. 441/449, 1979.

[5] *Hensen, F.* a. *H. Siemetzki:* Kunststoffe 70, pp. 753/758, 1980.

Continuous melt filtration systems

Michael Bevis

Design objectives

The main objective in the design of all of the Process Developments "Auto-screen®" extruder screen changers is to provide for uniform extrusion conditions, that is, to maintain a constant pressure drop across the filter pack. There are two main versions of the Autoscreen. The well established version [1] of which more than 1,500 have been supplied to industrial firms, and the new "Twin-Screen" version which has been specially made to meet arduous applications, such as, the filtration of severely contaminated polymers and the very fine melt filtration of polymers at constant pressure drop.

Other design objectives for both ranges of filters was to provide for automatic operation and minimal maintenance and technician involvement during extrusion operations. The continuous filter screen is the only moving part of the screen changer.

Constructional features

The Autoscreen features one-piece construction and is therefore leak proof. Stainless steel versions are obtainable where required. A continuous filter element is used for both versions and can be supplied in lengths up to 100 m. The filter element is uncut and is used in the as-woven state. Water cooled and electrically heated ports flank the filtration chamber, as illustrated in figure 1.

Principle of operation

Single screen

Molten polymer under a head pressure P is filtered through the element (screen) (2) which is backed by a conventional breaker plate (3).

Molten polymer also enters, through the gate (10) into the cooling chamber (4), where under the effect of circulating water the polymer solidifies and entraps the filter element in its middle. This hard polymer plug (5) inside

141

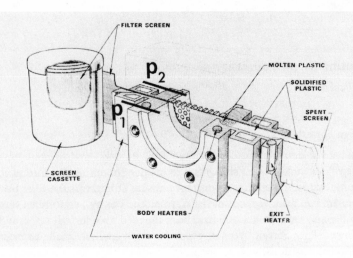

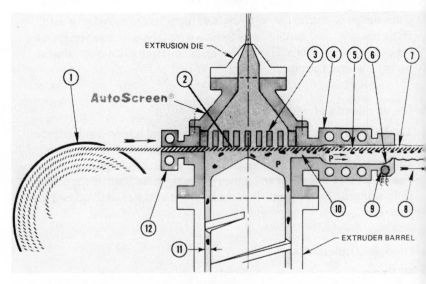

Fig. 1. The continuous concept screen changer.

the slot of the cooling chamber is squeezed forward, under the head pressure P and forms and leak proof polymer seal against the greatly reduced width of the exit port (7).

To the extent that the heater cartridge (9) is activated, some polymer will soften in the adjacent layers (6) and under the head pressure P, the cold polymer plug (5) will begin to slowly move, in the direction of arrow (8) (much as a piston moves between cylinder walls) as softened polymer will slowly be squeezed through exit port (7) out into the open.

By modulating the heat input from the heater cartridge (9) the rate at which polymer is being softened and squeezed through the port (7) and, accordingly, the rate at which the cold plug (5) will be moving outward can be readily adjusted. Turning the heater (9) off will stop the movement of the plug.

As the polymer plug slowly squeezes outward (8) it pulls along the filter element which is embedded in its middle. Accordingly, new screen is gradually pulled out from the canister (1) as the used up screen slowly moves in the direction of arrow (8) removing all foreign particles it has screened out from the melt flow.

Twin-Screen

The filter element in the Twin-Screen is parallel rather than perpendicular to the extrusion direction. The melt is caused to split into two routes as schematically illustrated in figure 2. The filter element consists of two complementary filters, which are supported against each other so that the pressure load is carried without a breaker plate. The transverse force acting on one filter is countered by a like force acting on the other filter and an inexpensive corrugated separator, which transfers the thrust between them and collects the filtered polymer which leaves edgewise between the filter elements. In this way the filter elements move with little resistance.

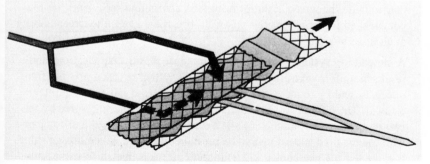

Fig. 2. The melt is caused to split into two routes as schematically illustrated.

The filter elements usually consist of multi-layer sandwiches of filter screens, which with the corrugated separator are provided in long reels.

The doubled filter area provided by the new geometry results in a very compact machine which is suitable for very large throughput, and retains the leakproof single-piece construction of the standard Autoscreen®.

In addition to the difference in orientation of the filter elements there are several other important differences in the designs of the standard and Twin-Screen versions of the Process Developments continuous melt filtration units. In the Twin-Screen some already filtered polymer is automatically injected and cooled as required to form a leak proof seal at the inlet port. The extrusion pressure is therefore contained by continuously reforming these sealing plugs. The other main difference is that the Twin-Screen is fitted with several exit and inlet sections. Separate control of the heating and cooling of these sections provides for more versatile operation of the machine. For example, there are three main modes of operation which illustrate the versatility of the exit sections.

a) Polyethylene – activate final section only

b) Nylon or polyester – stress annealing and overall detachment automatic techniques

c) Low pressure applications – modulate all exit sections – hot and cold.

Control Options

Three different control systems are offered for both versions of the Autoscreen and these automatically regulate the frequency and duration of the exit heater's operation, which controls the rate of screen movement.

The time-interval control may be used for relatively clean materials that contaminate the screen at uniform levels. A continuous feed control is recommended for more sensitive materials, because it keeps the screen moving at all times at a pre-set rate.

A closed-loop system is available for the most sensitive applications and results in uniform extrusion conditions. This system relies on pressure transducers P_1 and P_2 to monitor the melt pressure before and after the filter element. The difference $\Delta P = (P_1 - P_2)$ in pressure values measured by the two transducers is continuously and automatically monitored and compared with the required and set maximum pressure difference. When this set value is exceeded the heater(s) in the exit section(s) is activated to cause new screen to move forward and to reduce the pressure drop.

144

Special Features

a) Continuous filter movement provides unlimited filter area.

b) The filter element (sandwich) is the only moving part: no mechanical complications.

c) Filter element speed is automatically modulated so as to maintain constant extrusion pressure.

d) No motor nor hydraulics: screen is activated by melt pressure in the extruder.

e) Leakproof, simple one-piece construction.

f) Twin-Screen. Balanced pressure load without breaker plate for exceptionally fine filtration.

Technical Specifications

Standard Autoscreen.

Standard sizes (metric) 30, 45, 50, 60, 75, 90, 100, 120, 150 and 200 mm, plus corresponding inch sizes.

Twin-Screen.

There are two standard sizes 60 and 200 mm, having instantaneous filtering areas of 171 and 813 cm^2 respectively.

Adaptors and stainless steel versions of the screen changers are obtainable where required.

Typical Applications

The main application for the Autoscreen screen changers is for extrusion jobs where constant extrusion conditions are required, they find wide application in film blowing, manufacture of pipe, filaments and general section extrusions.

Specially designed versions of the standard machine can provide for filter element movement of 50 cms per hour when dealing with heavily contaminated material. For example, the Autoscreen has found application in the filtration of plasticised cable scrap. The Twin-Screen is designed to cope with high levels of contamination.

145

The standard Autoscreen will successfully filter a wide range of grades of high and low density polyethylene, PS, HIPS, PP, nylons, polyester etc to 60 μm. The Twin-Screen will filter the same range of materials for a greater ΔP and down to much finer mesh sizes. To give, for example, filtration to 20 μm in fibre recycling.

It is also possible to use the Autoscreen on flow moulding and injection blow moulding machines for the removal of impurity particles. Details of these applications and developments in these fields of application will be reported.

Economy of Application

A wide range of filter elements can be supplied for the Autoscreens, but usually Dutch twill is selected. Prices vary according to the mesh and types of weave. The filter elements are used in the as-woven state and do not have to be cut.

The economy of application is primarily determined by the selected control option and the pressure difference across the screen which is considered to be consistent with satisfactory extrusion conditions. This will vary from one extrusion job to another.

A major factor in the costing of melt filtration is the labour involved in screen changing and maintenance. The objective behind the design of the Autoscreens is to reduce the labour content involved in these operations by offering various levels of sophistication and automation.

Wear is not considered to be a problem with the Autoscreens. The sides of the Twin-Screen are hardened to Rockwell 70, and no wear has been observed in applications to date. The breaker plates on the standard models are specially designed to be reversible, but so far none of the many units sold with this design feature have required turning.

Material losses equal to a 2 cm thick slab per length of used screen do occur and solely comprise the polymer which entraps the filter element, and emanates from the exit port. The level of material loss will be determined by the selected control option, and will be least when the control option giving constant pressure conditions is adopted.

Bibliography

[1] *Murray, T. A.*: Extruder screen changers. The choices widen. Plastics Technology 65 (23) 1977.

Melt filters with continuous cleaning of the filter element

Werner E. Siemens

The filtration of thermoplastic polymer melts is difficult because of the high temperature, high pressure and high viscosity of these melts. Melt flow should not be disturbed by the removal of foreign particles, i. e. melt temperature and pressure should remain constant and the melt throughput per unit time should also remain unchanged. A filter whose surface gradually becomes clogged with contaminant particles is, however, anything but a constant size flow passage and, in order to meet the above requirements one must either constantly renew the filter element or find a way of cleaning it continuously. In the melt filter described below, the filter element is cleaned continuously by arranging for some of the melt to flow backwards inside the filter housing through a very small filter area, the resultant contaminant concentrate being discharged continuously.

This continuous filter, fig. 1, essentially consists of a housing (1), a pair of breaker plates (2 and 3), a central drive shaft (4) which can be driven hydraulically or electrically and a purging unit (5), which is in radial contact with the breaker plates, as shown in figs. 2 and 3. The purging unit is rotated slowly by the shaft, half to one revolution per minute having proved satisfactory. The filter element can be made of conventional wire

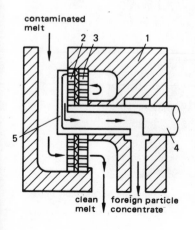

contaminated melt

2 3   1

5

4

clean melt | foreign particle concentrate

Fig. 1.
Diagram of Siemens filter, showing principle of operation.
1   housing
2 and 3 breaker plates
4   shaft
5   purging unit

Fig. 2. Siemens filter: breaker plate with purging unit.

Fig. 3. Siemens filter: solid, i. e. undrilled, area to accomodate purging unit in the stationary position.

mesh and is placed between the two breaker plates which hold it in position. The breaker plates are placed not at right angles to the melt stream but lengthways in the direction of the extruder. This makes it easier to rotate the purging unit and it also ensures that every contaminant particle must travel the same path, no matter where it passes through the filter. In this way one also achieves a uniform residence time in the case of large area filters, so that the entire melt stream is evenly heated.

The purging unit has a slit-like channel which passes into the open through the hollow-bored shaft. As the unit carries out its rotating movement across the top breaker plate it covers one row of holes against the melt pressure, so that these holes can be purged by the already filtered melt flowing backwards. The resultant contaminant concentrate passes to the centre through the channel of the purging unit, and thence into the open via the hollow shaft. One revolution of the purging unit thus results in the complete purging of the entire filter surface. Switching elements stop the purging unit after exactly one revolution by switching off the drive. In this stationary position of the purging unit, the breaker plates are not drilled, so that the flow channel is closed, and no melt passes through. Fig. 4 shows the drive

Fig. 4. Siemens filter: drive with limit switch.

with the limit switch, whilst fig. 3 shows the solid, i. e. undrilled area of the breaker plate for the purging unit in the stationary position. Because the purging unit drive shaft rotates so slowly, it is no problem to achieve an absolutely tight seal, whether by means of a stuffing box or a radial seal. The filters have proven absolutely tight even after being in use for a long time.

In order to clean a filter by recirculating clean melt it must be possible to easily remove the contaminant particles from the filter surface. The supporting screens should therefore not be too fine-meshed (which would prevent efficient recirculation) and the contaminant particles should not be pressed too firmly on to the filter surface. This means that one should not wait with melt recirculation until the filter has become clogged, and the melt pressure has increased considerably. An automatic control unit which initiates recirculation of the melt when the melt pressure has increased by 10 – 30 bar.

The purging unit covers about one-twentieth of the filter surface so that the melt stream is hardly affected even during the purging phase. The entire barrel is always filled by the melt to be filtered, so that there is no risk of the extrudate tearing due to interruption of the melt flow or occluded air.

Thanks to this filter, smooth, automated production has become possible even when melts contain a high proportion of contaminant. The following two examples are typical of what can be achieved in this direction.

1. In a blown film plant making high density polyethylene film in a range of sizes, including subsequent conversion into bags etc., it was planned to recycle the in-plant waste by re-compounding it and using it to produce blown film. The filter used had to be designed so that cleaning of the melt would not affect the film bubble and the film gauge tolerance would not exceed ± 2 %. A 90 mm extruder was used, and a filter of the above described design chosen, the screen diameter being 180 mm. The screen was made of a square mesh fabric with a mesh size of 100 μm, with a throughput of about 190 kg/h at a pressure of 200 bar. The automatic purging system was set so that the filter drive would switch on at 230 bar. The amount of material removed through purging was measured as 120 g in 2 minutes, so that the loss incurred during cleaning of the filter – and thus the reduction in film gauge – was less than 2 %. Purging was initiated once or twice per hour, depending on the degree of contamination.

2. Scrap from the production of spun nylon fibres had to be filtered and pelletised, Melted nylon 6.6 is a very thin liquid at 300 °C, making strand pelletisation somewhat difficult. Tearing of the strands would greatly inter-

150

fere with production and, on the other hand, spun fibre waste is often heavily contaminated so that filtration must be extra efficient. A 70 mm twin screw with vent section ensured a melt pressure of about 50 bar and a throughput of 100 kg/h. The shredded, dried scrap was fed to the extruder via a special stuffing unit.

The melt was passed through a strand die after being filtered with a Siemens filter of the above mentioned design, with a breaker plate diameter of 180 mm. The strand die produced 15 strands, each 3 mm in diameter. The automatic filtration unit switched to back-flow purging at 70 bar, the loss per purging amounting to 100 g. Up to six purgings were required per hour, depending on the amount of contaminant present. Stainless steel screens were used, with a mesh size of 60 μm. The screens were changed only once a week as a matter of routine, despite being in use for 24 hours a day.

Apart from being used for filtering polyethylene and nylon, these filters have proved suitable for a wide range of thermoplastics, ranging from the viscous ABS to the low viscosity polyacetals, from low-melting hot melt compounds to high-melting polyesters. The filter is not, however, suitable for PVC since this would degrade in the back-flow purging channel, thereby clogging it and putting it out of action.

The filters just described are at present being made in diameters of 150, 180 and 250 mm.

Wire mesh screens for filtering polymer melts

Gerhard Schönbauer

Wire gauze is widely used for making screens used to filter polymer melts and has specific, reproducible characteristics resulting from gauze parameters. Square-mesh gauze has a mesh size that is easy to determine and which remains constant within close tolerances, with accurately dimensioned holes and a permeability which remains constant over the entire suface. Besides wire gauzes with square or rectangular holes one also uses braided filter gauzes, i. e. wire gauze in which either the warp or the weft wires are so close together that a "zero mesh" is produced. Such gauzes are being successfully used for filtering polymer melts. The special structure of braided filter gauzes results in a extremely narrow scattering of hole widths, even under high mechanical loadings. This gives great accuracy in the separation of solid particles. By combining different types of wire gauze, it is possible to combine the special characteristics of the individual wire gauzes, e. g. in the form of screen packs.

Terms and definitions

The terms used in connection with wire gauzes are not always consistent. Let us therefore explain the most important terms and definitions.

Wire gauze	a flat product formed by woven wires.
Warp	all wires running parallel to the edges.
Weft	all wires running at right angles to the edges.
Wire diameter (d)	measured in the finished wire gauze in the projected gauze area.
Mesh	consists of two adjacent warp and weft wires and the screen opening they form.
Mesh width (w)	distance between two adjacent warp and weft wires, measured in the projected gauze area.
Spacing (t)	sum of mesh width and wire diameter ($t = w + d$).

153

Meshes/cm	number of meshes per 1 cm = 10 mm $\left(\dfrac{10}{t}\right)$.
Meshes/cm^2	$\left(\dfrac{10}{t}\right)^2 = \left(\dfrac{10}{w+d}\right)^2$.
Mesh/inch	number of meshes per inch = 25.4 mm.
	$\dfrac{25.4}{t} = \dfrac{25.4}{w+d}$
Count	number of meshes per distance differing from the inch, e. g. per 26, 26.16, 27 or 27.78 mm.

Relative free screen area (open screen area, degree of screen opening)

$$\left(\frac{w}{w+d}\right)^2 \times 100 = \left(\frac{w}{t}\right)^2 \times 100 \, (\%)$$

Weight per unit area
(kg/m^2) $\quad \dfrac{12.7 \, d^2}{t}$ (density of 7.85 kg/dm^3 for steel)

d = wire diameter in mm
t = spacing in mm ($t = w + d$)

The most important terms and abbreviations for wire gauze are contained in DIN 4185 [1].

Wire gauze used for filtering polymer melts is usually made from round-section metal wire, but for special applications one can also use oval or rectangular section materials. Round-section metal wires for wire gauze are standardised in DIN 4186 [2].

Differentiation of mesh widths

Here we would refer to ISO 2194 "Wire screens and plate screens for industrial purposes – Nominal sizes and apertures", according to which mesh sizes are exclusively differentiated according to the series R 10, R 20 and R 40, the basic foundations of which are contained in ISO 3 and DIN 323 [5].

The differentiation contained in DIN 4189, where wire gauzes made of steel, stainless steel and non-ferrous metal wire, with mesh widths of 0.025 to 16 mm are standardised, is primarily according to R 10, intermediate values having been taken from R 20 [4].

154

Table 1. Grouping of mesh widths according to standard number series (mesh widths 1 – 10 mm).

R 10	R 20	R 40	R 20/3	R 40/3
10	10	10		
		9,5		9,5
	9	9		
		8,5		
8	8	8	8	8
		7,5		
	7,1	7,1		
		6,7		6,7
6,3	6,3	6,3		
		6		
	5,6	5,6	5,6	5,6
		5,3		
5	5	5		
		4,75		4,75
	4,5	4,5		
		4,25		
4	4	4	4	4
		3,75		
	3,55	3,55		
		3,35		3,35
3,15	3,15	3,15		
		3		
	2,8	2,8	2,8	2,8
		2,65		
2,5	2,5	2,5		
		2,36		2,36
	2,24	2,24		
		2,12		
2	2	2	2	2
		1,9		
	1,8	1,8		
		1,7		1,7
1,6	1,6	1,6		
		1,5		
	1,4	1,4	1,4	1,4
		1,32		
1,25	1,25	1,25		
		1,18		1,18
	1,12	1,12		
		1,06		
1	1	1	1	1

Mesh widths for industrial screens in Britain and the USA are differentiated according to the standard series R 40/3.

The difference between the individual steps varies, depending on which series of numbers is used. For R 10 for example it is about 25 %, for R 20 about 12 %, for R 40 about 6 % and for the derived series R 40/3 about 18 %.

Every second figure from the series R 40/3 is contained in R 20 and gives the derived series R 20/3 with steps of about 40 %. These mesh widths are also contained in standard specifications which are exclusively divided according to R 10 and R 20, e. g. the standards of France and W. Germany.

The fundamental thought behind differentiation according to R 20/3 is that the mesh width that follows next has a surface area that is double that of the previous one. This results in a factor of $1 : \sqrt{2}$, with a differentiation of approximately 40 %. The intermediate figure after $\sqrt[4]{2}$ was introduced later on in order to achieve a closer differentiation. Table 1 lists the different mesh widths in the discussed series between 1 and 10 mm.

Mesh shape

Wire gauze is produced with different kinds of mesh shape. The most common shapes are:

Square mesh

The distance between the warp and the weft wires is equal, so that a square is formed.

Wide mesh

The distance between the warp wires is greater than that between the weft wires.

Longitudinal mesh

Here, the distance between the warp wires is smaller than that between the weft wires.

Wire gauze with longitudinal or wide meshes, i. e. with rectangular meshes allows greater variety as regards wire diameter and mesh width in warp and weft direction. Such gauzes are made on a large scale with plain as well as twill weave. In the latter case, longitudinal and wide mesh wire gauze can be made also with mesh sizes differing by less than 25 %. Such gauzes have proved to be extremely strong filter elements.

Zero mesh

Here the warp or the weft wires lie so close together that meshes are no longer visible in projection. Wire gauze with zero mesh are referred to as braided fabrics. The diameter of the largest spherical particle which will just pass through the braided fabric is called the fineness of the filter.

Wire cloth weaves

Wire cloth consists of wires woven in warp and weft direction, with uniform holes in between the wires. The way in which warp and weft threads cross one another is called the weave of the fabric or cloth. One distinguishes between three basic types of weave: plain, twill and satin weave.

For the filtration of polymer melts one normally uses plain or twill weave wire cloth, with four shafts (Z or S rib). Fig. 1 illustrates the different kinds of weave as well as stereo-scan photographs of the wire cloths most commonly used for filtering polymer melts, including braided filter fabrics [6].

Most square mesh wire cloth is made in plain weave, whilst very fine mesh material with a mesh size of less than 63 μm is usually made in twill weave, with four shafts (S or Z rib).

In plain weave, each warp wire is placed alternately above and below a weft wire, and the weft wire alternately above and below a warp wire. In four-shaft twill weave, S or Z rib, the warp wire lies alternately above and below two weft wires, and the weft wire alternately above and below two warp wires. The diagonal line formed by the weave is called the twill line. The letters S and Z are used to identify the direction of the twill line. This four-shaft twill weave is chosen when the wire is so thick in relation to the mesh width that it is not able to withstand the deformation produced during the weaving of a plain weave fabric.

Wire cloth with square meshes

Table 2 lists the most important wire gauze specifications for square mesh cloth with mesh sizes from 0.025 to 1.25 mm for filtering polymer melts. The table provides information on the following most important points:

Square mesh, plain weave

Wire gauze with square holes. The plain weave results in extremely accurate holes, making it the most widespread type of gauze.

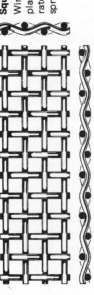

Square mesh, twilled weave

Wire gauze with square holes. The meshes can, however, be easily moved diagonally. Most fine fabrics with mesh widths of less than 63 μm and those made of specially thick wires.

Reverse plain Dutch weave (RPD)

RPD fabrics contain warp wires that are arranged extremely close together and are relatively thin, whilst the weft wires are much thicker. Characteristics: accurate filtration, high throughflow rate, low pressure loss. RPD fabrics are rough on both sides.

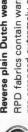

Broad mesh twilled Dutch weave (BMT)

Unlike DTW (see below) the weft wires are arranged loosely.
Characteristics: accurate filtration, high throughflow rate, moderate pressure loss. BMT fabrics are smooth on both sides.

Dutch twilled weave (DTW)

Here the weft wires are in twill weave and arranged very close together.
Characteristics: very accurate filtration, low throughflow rates, high pressure loss. DTW fabrics are smooth on both sides.

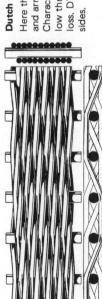

Single plain Dutch weave (SPW)

The weft wires are arranged very close together, in plain weave.
Characteristics: very accurate filtration, high throughflow rates, moderate pressure loss. SPW fabrics are rough on both sides.

Fig. 1. The most important types of wire cloth weaves.

Table 2. Square mesh wire cloths.

1	2	3	4	5	6	7	8	9	10	11
Mesh width ISO 2194-1972				Wire dia-meter	relative free screen area	Unit weight (steel)	Meshes per 1000 mm (accurate figure)	Meshes per cm² (approx. figure)	Meshes per inch (approx. figure)	Wire diameter (approx. figure)
Main series R 10	1st sec-ondary series R 20	2nd sec-ondary series R 40	μm	d	a_o	G	Nr.: m	M/cm²	Mesh	inch
w mm	w mm	w mm	w	mm	%	kg/m²				
0,025	0,025	0,025	25	0,025	25	0,16	20.000	40.000	500x500	.0010"
	0,028	0,028	28	0,025	28	0,15	18.868	36.000	480x480	.0010"
		0,03	30	0,025	30	0,14	18.182	33.000	460x460	.0010"
		0,03	30	0,028	27	0,17	17.241	30.000	440x440	.0011"
0,032	0,032	0,032	32	0,025	32	0,14	17.544	31.000	450x450	.0010"
0,032	0,032	0,032	32	0,028	28	0,17	16.667	28.000	425x425	.0011"
		0,034	34	0,03	28	0,18	15.625	25.000	400x400	.0012"
	0,036	0,036	36	0,028	32	0,16	15.625	25.000	400x400	.0011"
	0,036	0,036	36	0,03	30	0,17	15.152	23.000	385x385	.0012"
		0,038	38	0,025	36	0,13	15.873	25.000	400x400	.0010"
0,04	0,04	0,04	40	0,032	31	0,18	13.889	19.300	350x350	.0013"
		0,042	42	0,036	29	0,21	12.821	16.900	325x325	.0014"
	0,045	0,045	45	0,032	34	0,17	12.987	16.900	325x325	.0013"
	0,045	0,045	45	0,036	31	0,20	12.346	15.200	315x315	.0014"

0,05	0,05	0,05	50	0,036	34	0,19	11.628	14.000	300x300	.0014"
0,05	0,05	0,05	50	0,04	31	0,23	11.111	12.400	280x280	.0016"
		0,053	53	0,036	35	0,19	11.236	12.400	270x270	.0014"
	0,056	0,053	53	0,04	32	0,22	10.753	11.600	270x270	.0016"
		0,056	56	0,04	34	0,21	10.417	10.800	260x260	.0016"
0,063	0,063	0,063	63	0,04	37	0,20	9.709	10.000	250x250	.0016"
0,063	0,063	0,063	63	0,045	34	0,24	9.259	8.600	250x250	.0018"
0,063	0,063	0,063	63	0,05	31	0,28	8.850	7.800	230x230	.0021"
	0,071	0,071	71	0,045	38	0,22	8.621	7.500	220x220	.0018"
	0,071	0,071	71	0,056	31	0,31	7.874	6.400	200x200	.0023"
		0,075	75	0,036	46	0,15	9.009	8.100	230x230	.0014"
		0,075	75	0,05	36	0,25	8.000	6.400	200x200	.0021"
0,08	0,08	0,08	80	0,04	44	0,17	8.333	7.000	210x210	.0016"
0,08	0,08	0,08	80	0,05	38	0,24	7.792	6.000	195x195	.0020"
0,08	0,08	0,08	80	0,063	31	0,35	6.993	5.000	180x180	.0025"
		0,085	85	0,056	36	0,28	7.092	5.000	180x180	.0023"
	0,09	0,09	90	0,05	41	0,23	7.143	5.000	180x180	.0020"
	0,09	0,09	90	0,056	38	0,27	6.849	4.900	170x170	.0023"
	0,09	0,09	90	0,063	35	0,33	6.536	4.300	170x170	.0025"
	0,09	0,09	90	0,08	28	0,48	5.882	3.400	150x150	.0030"
0,1	0,1	0,1	100	0,063	38	0,31	5.135	3.600	155x155	.0025"
0,1	0,1	0,1	100	0,071	34	0,37	5.848	3.400	150x150	.0028"
		0,106	106	0,08	32	0,44	5.376	2.900	150x150	.0030"
0,112	0,112	0,112	112	0,08	34	0,42	5.208	2.700	130x130	.0030"

Table 2.

Main series R 10 w mm	1st secondary series R 20 w mm	2nd secondary series R 40 w mm	μm w	Wire diameter d mm	relative free screen area a_0 %	Unit weight (steel) G kg/m²	Meshes per 1000 mm (accurate figure) Nr.: m	Meshes per cm² (approx. figure) M/cm²	Meshes per inch (approx. figure) Mesh	Wire diameter (approx. figure) inch
	Mesh width ISO 2194-1972									
0,125	0,125	0,125	125	0,08	37	0,40	4.878	2.500	120x120	.0030"
0,125	0,125	0,125	125	0,09	34	0,48	4.651	2.200	120x120	.0037"
	0,14	0,14	140	0,112	31	0,63	3.968	1.600	100x100	.0045"
		0,15	150	0,1	36	0,51	4.000	1.600	100x100	.0040"
		0,15	150	0,112	33	0,61	3.817	1.500	100x100	.0045"
0,16	0,16	0,16	160	0,1	38	0,49	3.846	1.600	100x100	.0040"
		0,17	170	0,125	33	0,67	3.390	1.200	85x 85	.0050"
	0,18	0,18	180	0,125	35	0,65	3.279	1.000	80x 80	.0050"
	0,18	0,18	180	0,14	32	0,78	3.125	1.000	80x 80	.0055"
0,2	0,2	0,2	200	0,125	38	0,61	3.077	900	78x 78	.0050"
		0,212	212	0,15	34	0,79	2.762	760	65x 65	.0060"
	0,224	0,224	224	0,16	34	0,85	2.604	680	65x 65	.0065"
	0,224	0,224	224	0,2	28	1,20	2.385	560	60x 60	.0075"

| 1 | 2 | 3 | 4 | 5 | 6 | 7 | 8 | 9 | 10 | 11 |

0,25	0,25	0,25	250	0,16	37	0,79	2.439	576	62x 62	.0065"
0,25	0,25	0,25	250	0,18	34	0,96	2.326	540	60x 60	.0070"
	0,28	0,28	280	0,112	51	0,41	2.551	650	65x 65	.0045"
	0,28	0,28	280	0,22	31	1,23	2.000	400	50x 50	.0090"
		0,3	300	0,22	33	1,18	1.923	370	48x 48	.0085"
0,315	0,315	0,315	315	0,2	37	0,99	1.942	400	50x 50	.0080"
	0,355	0,355	355	0,25	34	1,31	1.653	270	42x 42	.010 "
0,4	0,4	0,4	400	0,125	58	0,38	1.905	350	48x 48	.0050"
0,4	0,4	0,4	400	0,25	38	1,22	1.538	256	40x 40	.010 "
		0,425	425	0,28	36	1,41	1.418	196	36x 36	.011 "
	0,45	0,45	450	0,28	38	1,36	1.370	188	35x 35	.011 "
0,5	0,5	0,5	500	0,2	51	0,73	1.429	190	36x 36	.0080"
0,5	0,5	0,5	500	0,32	37	1,59	1.220	144	30x 30	.013 "
0,5	0,5	0,5	500	0,36	34	1,91	1.163	135	30x 30	.014 "
	0,56	0,56	560	0,36	37	1,79	1.087	121	28x 28	.014 "
		0,6	600	0,4	36	2,03	1.000	100	25x 25	.016 "
0,63	0,63	0,63	630	0,25	51	0,90	1.136	132	29x 29	.010 "
0,63	0,63	0,63	630	0,4	37	1,97	971	100	25x 25	.016 "
	0,71	0,71	710	0,45	37	2,22	862	74	22x 22	.018 "
		0,75	750	0,5	36	2,54	800	64	20x 20	.020 "
0,8	0,8	0,8	800	0,5	38	2,44	769	59	20x 20	.020 "
		0,85	850	0,4	46	1,63	800	64	20x 20	.016 "
		0,85	850	0,5	40	2,35	741	55	20x 20	.020 "
0,9	0,9	0,9	900	0,36	51	1,31	794	63	20x 20	.014 "

Table 2.

1	2	3	4	5	6	7	8	9	10	11
Mesh width ISO 2194-1972				Wire dia-meter	relative free screen area	Unit weight (steel)	Meshes per 1000mm (accurate figure)	Meshes per cm² (approx. figure)	Meshes per inch (approx. figure)	Wire diameter (approx. figure)
Main series R 10	1st secondary series R 20	2nd secondary series R 40	μm							
w mm	w mm	w mm	w	d mm	a_o %	G kg/m²	Nr.: m	M/cm²	Mesh	inch
1		1	1.000	0,28	61	0,78	781	61	20x 20	.011 "
1		1	1.000	0,36	54	1,21	735	54	19x 19	.014 "
1		1	1.000	0,5	44	2,12	667	48	17x 17	.020 "
1		1	1.000	0,56	41	2,55	641	41	16x 16	.023 "
1		1	1.000	0,63	38	3,09	613	36	16x 16	.025 "
1		1	1.000	0,8	31	4,52	556	31	14x 14	.032 "
	1,12	1,12	1.200	0,36	57	1,11	676	48	17x 17	.014 "
		1,18	1.800	0,45	52	1,58	613	38	16x 16	.017 "
		1,18	1.180	0,63	43	2,78	552	31	14x 14	.025 "
1,25	1,25	1,25	1.250	0,4	57	1,23	606	38	15x 15	.016 "
1,25	1,25	1,25	1.250	0,8	37	3,96	488	25	12x 12	.032 "

Symbols and formulae for wire gauzes

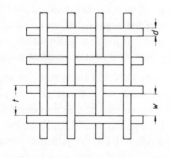

w = mesh width

d = wire diameter

t = spacing = w + d

a_0 = relative free screen area

mesh = mesh per inch = 25.4/t

Nr./cm = mesh per cm = 10/t

M/cm^2 = mesh per cm^2 = $(10/t)^2$

165

Mesh width, wire diameter, relative free screen area, unit weight, number of meshes per 1000 mm, number of meshes per cm^2, mesh and wire diameter in inches. Column 6 lists the mesh width and wire diameter, as well as the calculated values for the relative free screen area.

Square mesh wire cloths are noted for their large relative filtration area. For wire cloths with plain weave, such as are used for filtering polymer melts, this area is usually between 31 and 61 %. Even in the case of twill weave cloths this figure is normally at least 25 %. Wire screens made of plain weave gauze usually consist of wires whose diameter is smaller than the mesh width, for technical reasons.

The unit weight G has been calculated in column 7 for wire cloths made of steel (denity 7.85 kg/dm^3) according to the empirically determined formula

$$G = \frac{12.7\ d^2}{t}.$$

The number of meshes per 1000 mm (column 8) is given as an accurate figure, but the number of meshes per cm^2 (column 9) as approximate figure, according to normal practice so far. The figures for number of meshes per inch given in column 10 are also approximate, according to normal practice. Column 11 gives the wire diameters in inches.

The indication "meshes per cm^2" which is still frequently encountered in the plastics industry dates back to DIN 1171 "Wire cloths for test screens", issued in October 1926, which standardised wire cloths with mesh sizes of 0.06 – 6.0 mm for the first time in Germany.

In the first edition of DIN 1171, wire cloths were characterised by cloth index numbers which referred to the number of meshes per cm as well as per cm^2. Already in the second edition of this standard, in 1934, screen designations referred to the clear mesh width. The wire cloth specifications given in DIN 1171 were all for cloths made in plain weave, with a relative filtration area of about 36 % and a mesh width range of 0.06 – 1.5 mm.

The finest wire cloth according to DIN 1171 was made of wires with a diameter of 0.04 mm, with a mesh width of 0.06 mm. The spacing was therefore 0.06 + 0.04 = 0.10 mm. The number of meshes per cm is therefore 10 divided by 0.1 = 100. This gives us a figure of 10,000 meshes per cm^2. In the successor to DIN 1171, namely DIN 4188, which appeared in February 1957, the differentiation of mesh width according to the standard series R 10 and R 20 was introduced.

166

A standard specification for industrial wire cloths appeared in Germany for the first time in November 1953, this being DIN 4189. The presently valid edition, DIN 4189 part 1, was published in February 1968 and also has a differentiation of mesh width according to R 10 and R 20.

The original "10,000 mesh screen", with the specification mesh width 0.06 mm, wire diameter 0.04 mm has now been replaced by the wire cloth with a mesh width of 0.063 mm and a wire diameter of 0.04 mm, with 97 meshes per cm, i. e. about 9,400 meshes per cm^2.

Wire cloths are no longer defined by meshes/cm^2 alone since, for example, fine wire cloth is being made from different diameter wires – depending on requirements – for the same mesh width. The number of meshes per cm^2 therefore varies and for this reason it is always essential to quote mesh width and wire diameter.

When polymer melt passes through square or rectangular wire gauze, the melt flow is not deflected, in contrast to braided cloth.

The narrowest point for a spherical particle to pass through a square mesh fabric is near the surface and for this reason square mesh fabrics are referred to as filter screens with surface filtration characteristics. The mesh widths of "open" wire gauze can be determined by means of projection, by measurement with a magnifying glass or under the microscope.

Plain and twill weave braided fabrics

Braided filter fabrics are used on their own or in conjunction with square mesh fabrics for the filtration of polymer melts. One distinguishes between plain and twill weave braids [8]. In the former either the warp or the weft wires lie very close together, whilst in the latter one differentiates between twilled braid in which the weft wires are very close together so that one wire is always above and one wire underneath the warp wire, i. e. a "closed" braid, and an "open" braid in which the weft wires are not so close together, but are spaced out. Braided filter fabrics are noted for the fact that they can be designed specifically for special processing conditions and demands on flow resistance and the separating effect [9 – 11].

Fig. 1 shows the most important weaves for braided filter fabrics used for polymer melt filtration.

Reverse plain Dutch weave (RPD)

Here, the thin warp wires are arranged as close together as possible. The thicker weft wires can be arranged very close together or – if a high throughflow rate, with low flow resistance is required — more widely spaced. This type of fabric can also be made so that spherical particles are retained at the surface rather than inside. In most standard RPD fabrics the narrow part in the fabric is, however, determined by the arced triangle formed by two warp wires and the weft wire. RPD fabrics are made mainly in filter finenesses of $18 - 500$ μm, and they are also used in continuous filtration system in tape form.

Broad mesh twilled Dutch weave (BMT)

In BMT fabrics, the weft wires are not arranged close together. The screen fineness and flow resistance can be varied as required by varying the weft density. For this reason, it is necessary to quote the weft wire diameter when ordering screen fabrics, in addition to the number of wires per inch or 100 mm.

BMT filter cloths are produced mainly in finenesses of $22 - 50$ μm.

Dutch twilled weave (DTW)

In these fabrics, the weft wires are arranged as close together as possible. Addition of the weft wire diameters per 10 cm or 1" produces a figure that is about $5 - 15$ % higher than double the distance, due to the deformation of the woven wire. Compared with single plain Dutch weave fabrics (SPW), DTW fabrics have double the number of weft wires. DTW fabrics can also be woven with multiple warp wires lying parallel with one another.

DTW fabrics are normally produced in finenesses of $8 - 120$ μm and used for many different filtration applications. The special weave of DTW fabrics ensures that the screen openings show but little variation, so that accurate separation of solid particles is achieved. DTW fabrics do, however, have the highest flow resistance compared with other filter fabrics, with the same filter fineness.

Single plain Dutch weave (SPW)

In plain weave braids the weft wires are very close together so that a zero mesh structure is formed. The addition of weft wire diameters to 10 mm or 1" gives a value that is $6 - 12$ % higher because of deformation of the wire. The warp wires are thicker and arranged wider apart. SPW fabrics are also made with multiple warp wires lying parallel with one another.

168

For SPW fabrics, the same geometric considerations apply as to RPD fabrics, the difference being that in this case the thin wires form the weft and are flattened at the points of intersection. The diameter of warp and weft wires and the distance between the warp wires can be varied so that spherical particles are either retained on the wire gauze surface or only on the inside through the spatially arranged triangular apertures.

There are various mathematical models for the passage of spherical particles. Such models can be used to predict the size of particles that will be retained by the filter fabric, with certain simplifications [10, 11]. These calculations are an important aid in designing new braided fabrics.

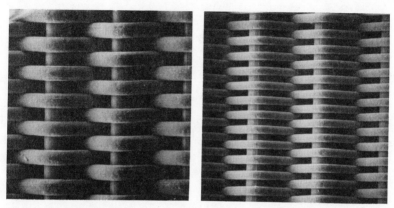

Fig. 2. Standard SPW filter fabric and high performance braided filter fabric.

In fig. 2 two braided filtration fabrics are compared, which differ only in that the weft wires are of different thicknesses. In the case of thin wires, the number of apertures per unit area necessarily increases. Furthermore, the triangular apertures become bigger and the throughflow resistance decreases. This type of fabric, which will also retain spherical particles already at the surface is often referred to as high performance filter fabric. The structure of these fabrics is shown in fig. 3.

Twilled reverse Dutch weave (TRD)

In this fabric, the warp wires which are usually thin and lying close together pass above and underneath two weft wires, so that the warp wires are not as much deformed as in the case of RPD fabrics. For continuous filtration sys-

169

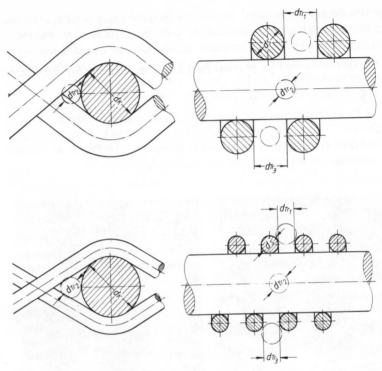

Fig. 3. Structural details of filter fabrics.

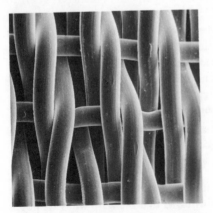

Fig. 4. Twilled reverse Dutch weave (TRD).

tems employing TRD tapes, it is also possible to use elastic warp wires. Such continuous screens can then be subjected to specially high loadings in warp direction. Fig. 4 shows a wire gauze specification using TRD fabric.

TRD fabrics are used for polymer melt filtration, normally for filter finenessses of 125 − 500 μm.

Characterisation of braided filter cloths

Braided filter cloths have not been standardised in Germany or by the ISO. For this reason there is no uniform method of characterisation.

The most common way of characterising these fabrics is by weave, mesh count and warp and weft wire diameters. Since braided fabrics are not characterised according to mesh width but filter fineness, this latter quantity can be expressed by a code number [8, 10, 11, 13, 15, 16].

One differentiates between absolute and relative filter fineness. The former is defined by the biggest spherical particles which can still just pass through the fabric. The latter is usually specified by the manufacturer of the filtration equipment and amounts to only a fraction of the absolute filter fineness. This is why widely different data are often given for a particular braided fabric. There is an urgent need for agreement on a uniform system.

This is an example of how an SPW type braided filter cloth is described:

SPW 125, 24 x 110 mesh, d = 0.36/0.25 mm

This means that the fabric, with an absolute filter fineness of 125 μm, has 24 wires per inch in the warp and 110 wires per inch in the weft. The warp wire diameter before weaving is 0.36 mm, the weft wire diameter 0.25 mm. The number of warp and weft wires can also be referred to 100 mm = 1 dm.

In a French draft standard the warp wire spacing and wire diameter in warp and weft are quoted as a means of characterising the fabric [12].

Materials used for wire cloths

The following materials are mainly used for making wire gauze for polymer melt filtration screens. These are also used in the rubber industry:

    bright steel
    galvanised steel
    spring steel
    stainless steel.

171

The most widely used material is stainless steel coded 1.4301 according to AISI 304, but stainless steels with code numbers 1.4401, 1.4541 and 1.4571 are also used.

Bright steel, galvanised steel and spring steel are used for the coarser kinds of wire gauze, especially square mesh gauze with mesh widths greater than 0.2 mm, such as are used for extruder screens. Wire cloths made of high strength spring steel wire have proved successful for round screens above 250 mm in diameter used in the rubber industry. These wires are three to four times as strong than normal steel wires and they can therefore be used in much thinner gauges for the same mesh width, so that the relative filtration area is made bigger [7].

Stainless steel wire is, however, preferred for making screens used for polymer melt filtration. These wire gauzes are used for circular and moulded screens and used in post-treated form. Fine wire gauze with a mesh width of 0.2 mm and less is bright annealed to make it completely flat, clean and strong. Wire gauzes with mesh widths of more than 0.2 mm are calendered to flatten them and increase their strength. If wire gauze has to be deformed or pleated, annealing has proved suitable also for mesh widths above 0.2 mm. In fact, annealing often makes tight pleating possible.

Stainless steel wire filter cloths best meet the demand for high strength, chemical and heat resistance.

Conclusions

Wire cloths with square meshes are clearly defined by the following:

    mesh width w

    wire diameter d

    weave

    material.

From this information, further data can be calculated, e. g. the relative filtration area, the unit weight, the number of wires per unit length etc. Porositiy can be determined experimentally if required or calculated under certain assumptions. It can also be obtained from diagrams. The mesh width and wire diameter of any given sample of wire gauze can be measured under the microscope or by projecting it on a profile projector.

In the case of fine mesh wire gauze (mesh width less than 200 μm), the wires for plain weave material are always thinner than the mesh width, for technical reasons. In the case of twill weave, fine wire gauze is made with

172

mesh width identical with wire diameter. The smaller the mesh width, the lower will be the mechanical loadability of the wire gauze for the same relative filtration area and the same initial strength of the wire. For this reason, fine and very fine screens are often used together with coarser screens to protect and support them.

Braided filter fabrics can be designed so that they have increased breaking strength in one direction. This means that the wires in that direction fulfil the demands for strength, whilst those lying in the other direction are arranged in accordance with filtration requirements. By varying the weaving technique it is thus possible to largely match the braided fabric to requirements. It is also possible to increase the number of holes in order to reduce throughflow resistance.

For plain braided fabrics, the number of apertures per cm^2 is 2 x the number of warp wires per cm x number of weft wires per cm. Using an approximation calculation for the base line and height of the traingular openings, this throughflow area can be related to the overall surface area, in our case 1 cm^2.

The percentage of filtration area is often referred to in the literature as the relative free cross-section [15]. A direct comparison with the relative free filtration area of square mesh fabrics is not appropriate since braided filtration fabrics deflect the melt flow.

The porosity of idealised, plain braided fabrics can also be theoretically calculated or read off from diagrams based on formulae relating to the ideal model [14].

With the help of these mathematical models it is possible to develop new braided filter cloths to meet requirements as closely as possible.

Bibliography

[1] DIN 4185, T. 1: Siebböden; Begriffe und Kurzzeichen für Gewebesiebböden. 07.1963.

[2] DIN 4186, T. 1: Siebböden, Runde Metalldrähte, Maße. 02.1968.

[3] ISO 2194-1972: Wire screens and plate screens for industrial purposes – Nominal sizes of apertures. First edition – 1972-02-15.

[4] DIN 4189, T. 1: Siebböden; Drahtgewebe aus Stahl-, nichtrostendem Stahl und NE-Metalldraht; Maße. 02.1968.

[5] ISO 3 – 1973: Preferred numbers – Series of preferred numbers. First edition – 1973-04-01.
     DIN 323, T. 1: Normzahlen und Normzahlreihen; Hauptwerte, Genauwerte, Rundwerte. 08.1974.

[6] Haver Spinndüsenfilter, Firmendruckschrift P 18, Haver & Boecker, 4740 Oelde, Carl-Haver-Platz, 1976.

[7] Haver Optiplan® Extrudersiebe aus Drahtgewebe, Firmendruckschrift P 74-78, Haver & Boecker, 4740 Oelde, Carl-Haver-Platz, 1978.

[8] Haver-Minimesh-Metalldrahtgewebe, Firmendruckschrift P 49-79, Haver & Boecker, 4740 Oelde, Carl-Haver-Platz, 1979.

[9] *Tittel, R. a. Berndt:* Faserforschung und Textiltechnik 27 (1976), p. 541.

[10] *Tittel, R. a. Berndt:* Faserforschung und Textiltechnik 24 (1973), p. 505.

[11] *Heidenreich, E., R. Tittel a. R. Berndt:* Aufbereitungs-Technik 18 (1977), p. 353.

[12] Document ISO/TC 24/SC 3 N 70 E/F; 1981.

[13] NASA-Final-Report WDP 200,.NAS 9 – 11264; Shuttle Filter Study, Volume I: Characterization and optimization of filteration devices. 1974.

[14] *Plaß, E.:* Chem. Ing.-Techn. 36 (1964), p. 747.

[15] *Schönbauer, G.:* Aufbereitungs-Technik 19 (1978), p. 217.

[16] *Junge, H.-P.:* Aufbereitungs-Technik 19 (1978), p. 209.

Wire gauze screens for filtering polymer melts

Gerhard Schönbauer

Wire gauze screens are widely used for filtering polymer melts, either singly or arranged in several layers. Such screen packs can contain up to 100 layers of wire gauze, depending on requirements. Fig. 1 shows the commonly used types of screen used for filtering polymer melts. Wire gauze filters may be divided into flat-bed filters and shaped filters.

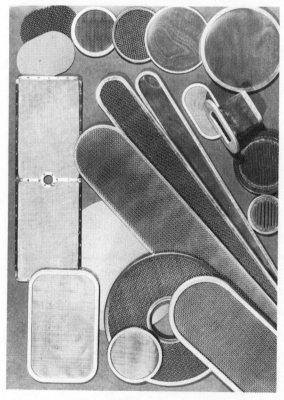

Fig. 1. Different types of wire gauze spinneret filters.

Flat-bed filters

Flat-bed filters consist of flat pieces of wire gauze and are made in the
following designs:

    circular filters
    long filters
    rectangular filters
    kidney-shaped filters
    annular filters
    beaded-edge filters.

These filters can be used with or without surround. Wire gauze intended
for filters without a surround is usually punched, braided filters are often
cut with a plasma arc. To ensure that the individual layers of wire gauze

Fig. 2.Wire gauze filters spot welded around the rim and with edge surround.

really lie flat after cutting, the gauze is often specially pretreated. Fine wire gauze, for example, is easiest to fabricate when it has been bright annealed, whilst coarser materials used for support or protection are usually calendered so that they lie flat after punching and are free from burr.

Multi-layer filter screens without a surrounding edge can be joined at the rim by spot welding. Filters consisting of one or more layers of wire gauze without a surround can be sealed with an extra aluminium frame.

Flat-bed filters are normally used with a surrounding edge which also seals them. The materials used for these surrounds include aluminium and alluminium alloy, stainless steel and nickel plated copper. To ensure a good seal one tries to use as soft a metal as possible although stainless steel has, of course, advantages from the point of view of wear resistance and ease of dismantling. One can also combine metals, e. g. by providing an aluminium surround with an additional stainless steel edge. Surrounds of circular filter screens can be flat or, in the case of aluminium, convex, the latter giving a better seal.

Fig. 2 shows a selection of circular, multi-layer filters. The filters without surround are shown with a spot-welded rim as well as plasma arc cut. The photograph also shows screens with different outside diameters, with a metal surround.

Fig. 3. Wire gauze filters with "closed" and "open" pleating.

Shaped filters

To increase the effective filter area, the filter elements can either be made in special shapes or made of pleated wire gauze in the form of circular or cartridge filters. Fig. 3 shows round filter screens with closed and open pleating.

Cartridge filters are also made in various designs from pleated wire gauze, e. g. with an exchangeable outer covering. Fig. 4 shows such an exchangeable, pleated cartridge filter. Different filter designs and sizes are used, depending on whether the filter element is to be used in the synthetic fibre industry for preliminary filtration (e. g. central melt filtration) or as spinneret filter (de-centralised melt filtration). Wire gauze filter screens for polymer melt filtration can also be combined with metal wire mats. Filter plates consisting of several layers of wire gauze joined by sintering are used for disc filters and cartridge filters.

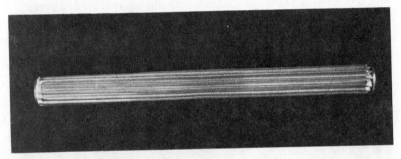

Fig. 4. Filter cover made of three-layer wire gauze, pleated.

Wire gauze combinations

Multi-layer wire gauze filters, also called multi-mesh filters, vary in structure, depending on requirements. Extremely fine wire gauze, which is decisive for the separating effect on the filter, can be combined with various layers of supporting gauze, this being arranged on the upstream or the downstream side. Apart from ordinary filtration, another purpose is the homogenisation of the polymer melt. For this one uses screen packs with up to 100 layers of wire gauze. The purpose of these many layers is not only to homogenise the melt but also to create space for the particles which have been filterd off, thereby preventing premature clogging of the extremely fine gauze.

Table 1 lists the standard combinations for circular filters used in spinneret extrusion.

Table 1. Possible wire gauze combinations for multi-layer spinneret filters.

2 wire gauze layers

Mesh size Mikrometer or	meshes per cm²	mesh
125	2.500	120 x 120
63	10.000	250 x 250
80	6.000	195 x 195
315	400	50 x 50
42	16.900	325 x 325
160	1.600	100 x 100
500	144	30 x 30
42	16.900	325 x 325
280	400	50 x 50
32	BMT 32	200 x 600
280	400	50 x 50
75	6.400	200 x 200
280	400	50 x 50
42	16.900	325 x 325

3 wire gauze layers

Mesh size Mikrometer or	meshes per cm²	mesh
160	1.600	100 x 100
80	6.000	195 x 195
200	900	78 x 78
315	400	50 x 50
80	6.000	195 x 195
160	1.600	100 x 100
63	10.000	250 x 250
80	6.000	195 x 195
315	400	50 x 50
200	900	78 x 78
40	19.300	350 x 350
63	10.000	250 x 250
40	DTW 40	80 x 700
75	6.400	200 x 200
280	400	50 x 50
280	400	50 x 50
75	6.400	200 x 200
42	16.900	325 x 325
850	64	20 x 20
280	400	50 x 50
42	16.900	325 x 325
500	144	30 x 30
280	400	50 x 50
75	6.400	200 x 200
280	400	50 x 50
63	10.000	250 x 250
42	16.900	325 x 325
224	560	60 x 60
80	6.000	195 x 195
42	16.900	325 x 325
280	400	50 x 50
75	6.400	200 x 200
224	560	60 x 60

4 wire gauze layers

Mesh size Mikrometer or	meshes per cm²	mesh
200	900	78 x 78
80	6.000	195 x 195
50	14.000	300 x 300
160	1.600	100 x 100
200	900	78 x 78
80	6.000	195 x 195
42	16.900	325 x 325
160	1.600	100 x 100
200	900	78 x 78
42	16.900	325 x 325
90	4.900	170 x 170
200	900	78 x 78
200	900	78 x 78
63	10.000	250 x 250
42	16.900	325 x 325
160	1.600	100 x 100
40	19.300	250 x 250
200	900	78 x 78
125	2.500	120 x 120
63	10.000	250 x 250
1.000	61	20 x 20
400	256	40 x 40
25	RPD 17	630 x 130
400	256	40 x 40
850	64	20 x 20
224	560	60 x 60
80	6.000	195 x 195
42	16.900	325 x 325

5 wire gauze layers

Mesh size Mikrometer or	meshes per cm²	mesh
160	1.600	100 x 100
42	16.900	325 x 325
32	31.000	450 x 450
63	10.000	250 x 250
200	900	78 x 78

6 wire gauze layers

Mesh size Mikrometer or	meshes per cm²	mesh
160	1.600	100 x 100
42	16.900	325 x 325
32	31.000	450 x 450
63	10.000	250 x 250
200	900	78 x 78
800	59	20 x 20

Materials

The standard material for wire gauze screens used to filter polymer melts is stainless steel which has the necessary strength, corrosion and heat resistance. The austenitic 18/8 CrNi steels with code numbers 1.4301, 1.4306 and 1.4541 are suitable for most purposes. The likewise austenitic CrNiMo steels coded 1.4401, 1.4404 and 1.4571 are used where increased resistance to reducing acids or chloride salt solutions is required.

If spinneret filters are used only once, which is usually the case, 18/8 CrNi steels are adequate. If they are to be used repeatedly, the 18/10/2 CrNiMo steels offer advantages.

Materials 1.4541 and 1.4571 are titanium stabilised variants and the minimum wire diameter for use in screens is 0.25 mm. They should only be used if the filter is to be welded or some other kind of heat treatment is used which could lead to intercrytalline corrosion — which is not, however, the case with spinneret filters. Table 2 compares the most important German and foreign standard designations for stainless steels used for wire gauze. In many cases the old Krupp names are still being used and these, too are therefore given in the table.

Table 2. The most important stainless steel grades for wire gauze, together with the comparable grades in Great Britain and the USA.

steel-iron list SEL	Krupp designation	USA AISI	Great Britain BS 970	Max. carbon content % C	steel composition according to SEL chromium % Cr	nickel % Ni	molybdenum % Mo	titan % Ti
1.4301	V2A-Supra	304	304 S 15	0,07	17,0–20,0	8,5–10,5		
1.4306	V2A-Supra NK	304 L	304 S 12	0,03	17,0–20,0	10,0–12,5		
1.4541	V2A-Extra	321	321 S 20	0,10	17,0–19,0	9,0–11,5		$\geq$ (5
1.4401	V4A-Supra	316	316 S 16	0,07	16,5–18,5	10,5–13,5	2,0–2,5	
1.4404	V4A-Supra NK	316 L	316 S 12	0,03	16,5–18,5	11,0–14,0	2,0–2,5	
1.4571	V4A-Extra	316 Ti	320 S 17	0,10	16,5–18,5	10,5–13,5	2,0–2,5	$\geq$ (5

Testing of wire gauze filters

Filter elements used to filter polymer melts should have a uniform pore size and pore size distribution. It is a major advantage of wire gauze that it has sharply defined holes over the entire area. Non-destructive tests for maximum pore size have shown that pore size is inversely proportional to the so-called bubble point test pressure. For this reason, wire gauze and wire

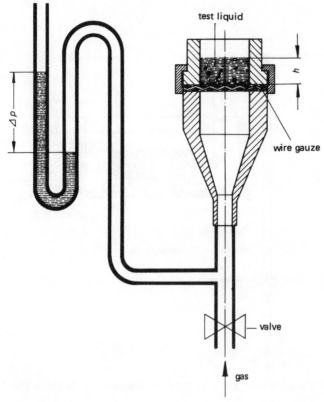

Fig. 5. Schematic drawing of the bubble point test for determining pore size of wire gauze filters.

gauze inserts as well as the actual filters can be tested by the bubble point method, the general set-up of which is shown in fig. 5. The test set-up for filter inserts is shown in fig. 6. Flow resistance can also be measured by means of throughflow determinations, and used for testing wire gauze filters.

Conclusion

Wire gauze and wire gauze filters are noted for sharply defined and easily ascertainable mesh or pore sizes which do not vary over the entire gauze area.

By combining several layers of wire gauze of the same or different fineness, it is possible to match the filter performance to specific requirements.

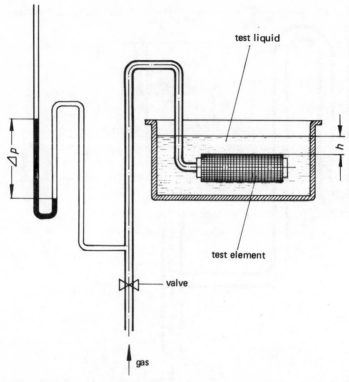

Fig. 6. Determination of maximum pore size of filter elements using the bubble point test.

Combinations with other filter media such as metal mats are likewise possible. The characteristics of the individual wire gauze layers can be positively influenced by special treatment of the gauze. The various layers can also be firmly joined by sintering. By combining various kinds of wire gauze it is possible to arrive at the best possible solution for any given production problem.

Bibliography

[1] Haver Spinndüsenfilter, Data Sheet P 18, Haver & Boecker, D−4740 Oelde, 1976.
[2] *Junge, H.-P.:* Aufbereitungstechnik 19 (1978), p. 209.
[3] ARP 901 (Aerospace Recommended Practice), Society of Automotive Engineers, Inc., 3.1 − 1968: Bubble Point Test Method.
[4] *Ehrhardt, G.:* Aufbereitungstechnik 22 (1981), p. 374.

182

Mats and sintered materials as filter media

Lothar Albano-Müller and Rainer Röhlig

The feature that is characteristic of all materials produced by powder metallurgical techniques as opposed to those made by metal fusion is their porosity. At one end of the porosity range which, in powder metallurgy, is 0.02 − 90 %, are sintered metal parts. The lower the pore content,

Table 1. Classification of sintered materials according to "SINT groups".

Material group	volume ratio $R_X = \rho_S / \rho_{th} \times 100\%$	Porosity $P = 100\% - R_X$	Typical applications
AF	< 73	> 27	filters, fire barriers, throttles
A	75 ± 2,5	25 ± 2,5	sliding bearings
B	80 ± 2,5	20 ± 2,5	sliding bearings, seals, guide rings, mouldings for light loads
C	85 ± 2,5	15 ± 2,5	sliding bearings, slide rings, medium-strength structural components e. g. bumper parts, oil pump gear wheels
D	90 ± 2,5	10 ± 2,5	high strength structural components for high stationary and moderate dynamic loads
E	94 ± 1,5	6 ± 1,5	very high strength structural components for high stationary and high dynamic loads
F	> 95,5	< 4,5	hot press moulded components for maximum loads
G	> 92	< 8	synthetic resin or metal impregnated components with good corrosion resistance, impermeable to oil and water
S	> 90	< 10	hot press moulded sliding bearings and sliding elements with incorporated solid lubricant

the higher will be the mechanical strength and elongation of the material. For maximum mechanical strength a density amounting to 99.9 % of the theoretical value is achieved through high temperature compression of blanks that habe been pre-compressed at room temperature. Only more or less tolerated in the case of moulded parts, porosity assumes great importance in sintered sliding bearings. The system of interconnected pores or cells serves as a means of storing oil and as an hydraulic system, and thus makes the bearings self-lubricating.

At the other end of the porosity range of sintered products, porosity is not only important but vital, in that it allows such products, made by powder metallurgy, to be used as filters. Here, the required pore content is greater than 27 % and is included in group SINT-A (table 1). The maximum pore content of filters made from powdered metal is today around 60 %, that of filters made fom sintered fibres as high as 90 %.

Raw materials for sintered metal filters

The quality of a filter element is determined not by the total pore content but by the number of pores which are open an both sides, i. e. which will let materials pass through. The so-called internal porosity and pores closed at one end are unwanted since they do not contribute towards the filter's efficiency. The filter area is increased. To prevent the formation of internal

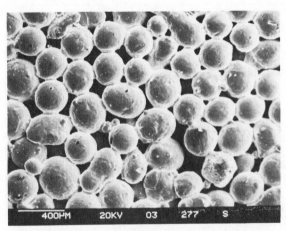

Fig. 1. Scanning electron micrograph of a sintered bronze filter made from spherical particle bronze powder.

184

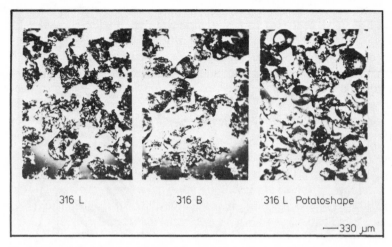

316 L   316 B   316 L Potatoshape

——330 μm

Fig. 2. Irregularly shaped stainless steel powder particles (material No. 1.4404).

pores and pores open only at one end, it is important to start off with powder particles of uniform size and the right shape. Bronze is easily converted into a powder by forcing it through fine jets (figs. 1 and 2). Bronze filters have been long established as an important product of powder metallurgy.

Filters made of stainless chrome-nickel steel have achieved great importance, especially in the chemical industry. When these materials, e. g. 316 L and 316 B are forced through a jet, irregularly shaped particles are usually formed, see fig. 2. Such particles, though advantageous from the processing point of view, have a strong influence on the filter's permeability because of

— a higher proportion of internal pores and pores closed at one end,
— a much branched network of pores,
— rough particle surfaces and pore walls.

All three influencing factors reduce permeability and increase the pressure loss. A branched pore network and surface roughness are, however, important for the special functions of porous parts, e. g. for retarding flame spread and as soundproofing agents.

Powder made from chrome-nickel steels (316 L and 1.4404) have lately become available. The particles are convex on all sides and smooth, and they are referred to having a "potato shape".

185

Chemische Zusammensetzung [Gew.-%]	C	Cr .	Mn	Mo	Ni	Si	Fe
	<0,03	16-18	<0,08	2,0-2,5	12-14	< 1,0	Rest

Φ 65 μm	Φ 150 μm	Φ 250 μm

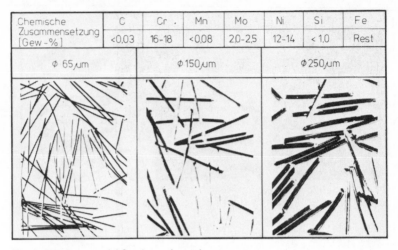

Fig. 3. Starting material for sintered metal mats.

Pure nickel, Hastelloy, Monel, Inconel and Incoloy are of special importance among the materials used for making filters, although titanium, tungsten, tantalum and other metals are nowadays also being used for making filters for special applications.

The production of sintered elements from chopped wire or fibres (fig. 3) may be regarded as an extension of powder metallurgy. Fibres made from chrome-nickel steel, pure nickel of other alloys, between 4 and 100 μm thick and 20 – 30 mm long, are made into non-woven mats and then sintered with a coarse wire gauze support. The high pore content of up to 90 % of these materials makes them very effective filter media, with a very low pressure loss.

There is no possibility of internal pores or pores closed on one side being formed.

Shaping

Figs. 4 – 6 show a selection of sintered metal filters. All known techniques of shaping, used in powder metallurgy, may be used to produce sintered filters except high temperature moulding, i. e. vibration sintering, conventional moulding (fig. 4) and isostatic moulding (figs. 5 and 6) followed by sintering, paste processing etc. In all such shaping operations it must be

186

Fig. 4. Stainless steel filters made by conventional compression moulding (material No. 1.4404).

remembered that a sintered metal filter is a body with a definite shape. Mechanical loads must therefore be absorbed by the filter medium.

In contrast to moulded parts and bearings, the important point as far as filters are concerned is not the dimensional stability of the parts but the pore size and pore size range. The quality of a filter is governed by the ratio of filter fineness (the effective pore size) of the separation rate to the pressure loss or permeability. The efficiency L can therefore be calculated from the product of filter fineness F and throughflow V, of the quotient of filter fineness F and pressure loss Δp:

$L = F\dot{V}$ or $L = F/\Delta p$

Fig. 5. Isostatically moulded, seamless filters with star-shaped cross-section (material No. 1.4404).

The filter efficiency L is dependent upon such factors as powder particle shape, size and size distribution, as well as on the moulding process employed, density and filter wall thickness in the direction of flow. Sintering conditions are also important to a limited extent, high temperatures and long sintering times improving mechanical properties, although they slightly reduce porosity.

The aim of the moulding or shaping process therefore is to achieve the best possible ratio between filter fineness and pressure loss, coupled with sufficient mechanical strength.

188

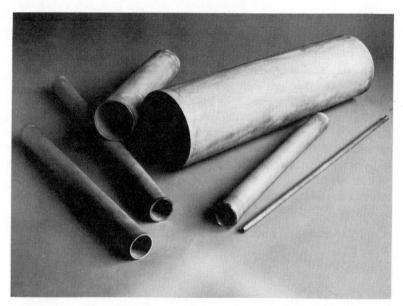

Fig. 6. Isostatically moulded, seamless filter tubes made of material Nr. 1.4404.

As we have already mentioned, spherical powder particles are best for achieving maximum filter efficiency. Since, however, this particle shape does not permit intermeshing of the particles among one another, moulding cannot impart dimensional stability of the part. Moulding must therefore occur simultaneously with sintering.

Vibration sintering means pouring the powder into a graphite or steel mould which is then vibrated to settle the powder. The mould and contents then passes through the oven. Because of the low sintering temperature of bronze, selecting the mould material presents no problems. The drawbacks of the method, e. g. large numbers of moulds for mass production and little possibility of automation, are countered by the advantage that the equipment used is inexpensive. Unlike conventional moulding techniques, this method allows threads and undercuts, as well as long, thin-walled pipes to be produced.

Related to vibration sintering is the so-called *paste process*. Here, the powder is made into a paste, using a binder which is usually organic, shaped without pressure in a mould in which it then dried or cured. This is followed

189

by burning or vapourising the binder and immediately sintering, so that the shape of the article remains intact. This process is used only for special cases where filters must be made from very fine powders and with a thin section.

The combination of moulding with binders and compression opens up the possibility of using high melting metal powders with spherical particles. Vibration sintering cannot be used in this instance because the higher sintering temperatures would cause problems for the mould material. Nor can pure paste processing be used for parts which have to withstand high mechanical loads and which must therefore be thick-walled. The advantages of, for example, chrome-nickel steel with the efficiency of bronze filters can only be combined by the *compression moulding of powders mixed with binder,* the powders consisting of particles which are smooth and convex on all sides.

In order to increase the porosity of such a filter, fillers may be incorporated to keep further pores, of controllable size, open. The filler vapourises

Fig. 7. Isostatic moulding plant.

during sintering, so that the number of pores will have been increased, depending on the apparent density of the powder.

To make filter elements from stainless steel, compression moulding, followed by sintering, has achieved the greatest importance. Apart from the already mentioned powders composed of spherical particles, mixed with binder, one now also uses powders consisting of irregularly shaped particles which tend to intermesh with one another, thus imparting sufficient strength to the moulded part. A disadvantage is however increased pressure loss due to reduced porosity and the greater proportion of closed pores.

To make large filters, especially long tubes and candles, which cannot be made in conventional moulds with uniaxial moulding movement, one now uses *isostatic moulding* with which filter elements up to 1500 mm long and 350 mm in diameter can be moulded in one piece (fig. 7). The characteristic feature of this technique is that the moulding pressure is transferred by a fluid. The homogeneous density distribution along the length of a pipe is ensured by the fact that the powder is poured into the space formed by a steel core surrounded by a flexible jacket, followed by vibration and application of pressure on all sides, using a moulding press. Filter candles and cylinders made in this way have been used for a long time in the chemical industry, but it is only the development of isostatic moulding which has made it possible to produce seamless parts. The method used hitherto, namely to bend and weld a conventionally compression moulded sheet to from candles or tubes, has several disadvantages. The weld reduces the strength of the filter immediately next to it and also reduces the effective filter area. When sheets are rolled into cylinders, there is the risk of cracking and changing the shape of the pores.

Even though the surface finish of a filter pipe is of secondary importance, a smooth surface is occasionally required. Because of the nature of the mould however, the surface produced by the flexible part will be much rougher than the side nearest the steel core. If a smooth outher surface is wanted for a pipe or candle, the process may be reversed, i. e. the powder is forced into the space formed by a flexible inner core and an outer steel pipe. The latter must, however, be in two parts to facilitate removal of the article.

When chrome-nickel steel fibres are processed, this is not done by any shaping process that is comparable to press moulding. The raw material, supplied in the form of bonded or non-woven mats of varying thickness is only rolled, cut, made into circular pieces or welded into cylinders after

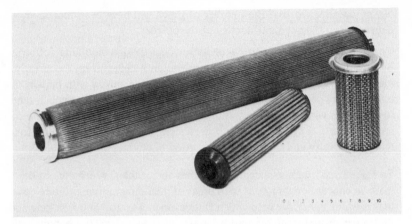

Fig. 8. Filter elements made of sintered metal fibre mats, used for filtering thermoplastic polymer melts. (material No. 1.4404).

sintering. This very flexible material can also be pleated, i. e. folded, thereby increasing the effective filter area if the filter has to be built into a fixed space, fig. 8. In this type of filter a suitable support must be provided to prevent it being deformed.

The purpose of a more recent development is to compression mould and sinter thicker, short wires made of chrome-nickel steel. Here, too, the special advantage is that no closed or partly closed pores are produced so that filtration efficiency is very high. The smooth, uniform wires produce a smaller pressure drop than powder filters and also have greater strength and resistance to back-flow. The combination of wires and powders also offers advantages as regards filter efficiency.

Sintering

Sintering is the process which imparts mechanical strength to the filter, although its specific filter characteristics are already determined at the moulding stage. Although fibre filters are not mechanically stiffened through sintering, this process causes the individual fibres to be fused to each other so that their position is fixed at very many points – a distinct advantage over woven wire gauze filters. The pore size – equivalent to mesh size in gauzes – is therefore unchanged so that a larger solid particle pressed against a pore by the melt pressure cannot pass through: there is no mesh

192

to be widened. This sintering method is identical with that used for making other powder metallurgical products where it is only the size of the items which often necessitates the use of large ovens, vacuum or an inert gas atmosphere. The temperature range lies between 800 °C for bronze filters and 1 280 °C for high grade Steel filters and is thus the normal sintering range.

Sintered filters should be machined only to make contact surfaces or cut threads. The effective filter surface should not, however, be tampered with – either by machining or non-cutting methods, although it is possible, in special instances, to open up pores which have become clogged by machining, e. g. grinding. This can be done by acid etching.

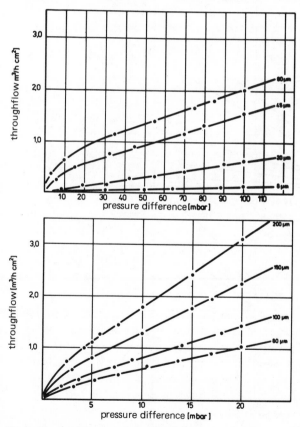

Fig. 9. Permeability of bronze filter elements.

Filter characteristics

The quality of filters is judged not only according to strength and dimensional stability but, above all, by their characteristic data such as filter fineness, pore size and permeability or pressure loss for a given throughflow. The pressure loss at constant volume troughput is dependent upon the number of pores and their size, i. e. from the effective cross-section (figs. 9 – 12). Volume throughput, i. e. permeability, depends on the available pressure difference and increases asymptotically. The permeability descreases almost linearly with increasing filter thickness. The filter permeability can be easily determined with air. The quantities measured are the preliminary

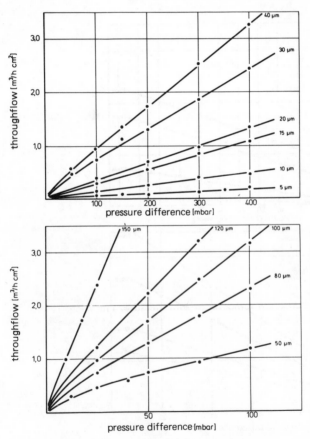

Fig. 10. Permeability of stainless steel filter elements.

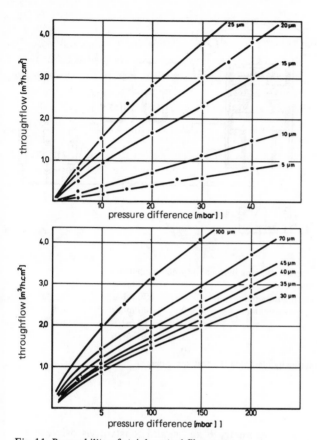

Fig. 11. Permeability of stainless steel fibre mats.

pressure p_1 and the pressure difference $\Delta p = p_1 - p_0$ and the volume of air passing through at constant temperature and pressure. The viscosity of the flowing medium is an important quantity for the volume throughput as a function of pressure difference. Darcy's equation shows the relationship between the quantities:

$$\Delta p = \frac{\dot{V} s \eta}{F \alpha}$$

where $\dot{V}$ = volume throughput, s = wall thickness in flow direction, η = dynamic viscosity of the flowing medium, F = area upon which medium

195

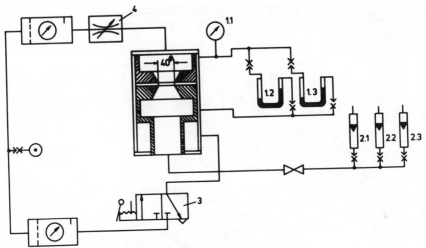

Fig. 12. Schematic diagram showing permeability determination.

1.1 inlet pressure manometer	0 – 10000 mbar
1.2 pressure difference manometer	0 – 100 mbar
1.3 pressure difference manomater	0 – 1000 mbar
2.1 flowmeter	0 – 10 m³/h
2.2 flowmeter	5 – 30 m³/h
2.3 flowmeter	10 – 100 m³/h

3. device for pneumatically clamping the test specimen
4. control valve

is flowing. For the given geometry F and s, and constant viscosity, α is the original slope of the determined curve $\dot{V}\,(\Delta p)$.

The Darcy equation has been derived from the Hagen-Poiseuille law of laminar flow through a pipe:

$$\Delta p = \frac{8\,\dot{V}\,\eta\,L}{\pi\,r^4}$$

Where L = pipe length, r = internal pipe radius. If one makes the pipe length and filter wall thickness equal and assumes that the filter surface in contact with the medium has N open pores with an average radius r, the following equation applies after the introduction of the correction factor K to take into account geometric simplification and inadequacies:

$$\Delta p = \frac{8 \, \dot{V} \eta \, s}{N \, \pi \, r^2} \times \frac{K}{r^2} = \frac{\dot{V} \eta \, s}{F} \times \frac{8 \, K}{r^2}$$

The second term is called the permeability $\alpha = r^2/8K$.

Compressible media in particular obey Darcy's equation only insufficiently — especially at high flow speeds. To better describe conditions, Forchheimer therefore introduced a higher order correction:

$$\Delta p = \frac{\dot{V} \eta \, s}{F \, \alpha} + \frac{\dot{V}^2 \, \rho \, s}{F^2 \, \beta}$$

The secound term takes the density ρ of the flowing medium into account and contains a second constant β which may be referred to as a turbulence coefficient. This quadratic term takes in the deviation from Darcy's equation, without the transition from laminar to turbulent flow being physically definable. In order to take this situation into account, the linear part of the pressure loss is referred to as frictional loss, the quadratic term as inertia loss.

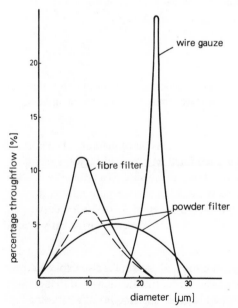

Fig. 13. Pore size distribution for different kinds of filters (according to Cole).

The flow conditions in the capillary system of a sintered filter are so complex that the transition point from laminar to turbulent flow cannot be fixed with any certainty, i. e. a critical flow speed and Reynolds number cannot be given. The coefficient β is never infinite, so that the second term never equals zero. It can however be ignored in many cases.

The second important filter quantity is the pore width and the number of pores per diameter, i. e. the pore size distribution (fig. 13). The ideal filter would only have pores of one size. Powders can however only be made with a certain particle size range and can only be used in that form for economic reasons. Moreover, the particle shape usually deviates to a greater or lesser extent from the spherical form so that for this reason, too, one must always accept a range of pore sizes which however is narrower than the particle size range. Filters made from spherical particle powders such as bronze filters are noted for a relatively narrow pore size spectrum, whilst that of high grade steel filters, made from irregularly shaped particles, is much broader. The range of wire gauzes and also that of fibre filters is much narrower than that of powder filters.

There are three methods that can be used for determining pore spectra:
1. The direct metallographic measurement of the pores,
2. porosimetry and
3. Cole's sigma flow method.

Using method 1 one obtains a sufficiently accurate distribution only through statistical summation, i. e. in several stages, which is a very long and complicated operation.

Method 2 is facilitated by the high surface tension of mercury. The pores of a test specimen dipped in mercury are filled with the substance, depending on the environmental pressure. Relating the pressure to a pore cross-section produces absolutely accurate results along the entire length only in the case of smooth, round pores with uniform cross-section. Distribution curves can, however be determined with good approximation also for irregularly shaped pores.

The relationship between surface tension and pressure is also exploited by Cole's sigma flow method. The porous body, filled with a fluid that completely wets it, is exposed to air on one side. The amount of air passing through the specimen is measured simultaneously with the pressure difference

198

in front of and behind the filter. One obtains a function between troughflow and pressure difference with the maximum values of bubble point and permeability of the dry test specimen. From the maximum pore size as fixed by the bubble point one can then determine the pore size distribution. This method of determination is relatively easy and can be accomplished without a great deal of apparatus. The results obtained may be used for production control purposes.

To measure the absolute pore size, i. e. the relevant diameter, one uses the glass bead test. The filter is subjected to a flow of glass beads with known particle size distribution and under specified conditions, e. g. in a stream of water. Measurement of the biggest beads to pass through the filter gives us the diameter of the biggest pore.

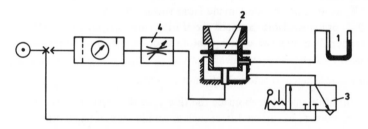

Fig. 14. Schematic diagram of the bubble point test
1. differential pressure manometer 0–500 mm water column
2. isopropyl alcohol
3. device for pneumatically clamping the test specimen
4. control valve

Much simpler in its execution, and quicker, is the so-called bubble point method, which is suitable for production control (fig. 14). As in the mercury test one makes use of the surface tension of a medium. One measures the pressure difference which has to be applied in order to force a test fluid from the biggest pores of a filter, using air. The pressure at which the first air bullbles issue from the filter immersed in this test fluid, gives us a measure of the largest pore cross-section. To relate the pressure difference to the pore diameter one needs to know not only the surface tension but also the angle of contact and the deviation of the pore cross-section from the circular shape. It is best to carry out the determination in a completely wetting medium. The form factor is best determined with the glass bead test.

199

Properties of sintered metal filters

Metal filters made by sintering metal powders have the following characteristics:

— Rigidity, i. e. they are self-supporting structural elements even at high pressure differences of the flowing medium. Maximum pressure difference 300 bar.

— Good resistance to vibration, impact and shock compared with ceramic filters which are much inferior in their mechanical properties at identical filter capacities or which have smaller filter capacities at identical mechanical properties.

— Excellent resistance to high temperature and temperature changes. Bronze filters can be used up to 400 °C, high grade steel ones up to 600 °C whilst certain filters made from special metals will withstand 1000 °C or higher. Here, sintered metal filters are superior to all organic materials and, in the case of temperature fluctuations, also to ceramic filters.

— Chemical resistance to acids, alkalis and solvents.

— Since filtration occurs deep inside the filter, particle separation is complete, in contrast to surface filters such as textile fabrics, paper and wire gauze.

— Wide range of pore sizes, from $0.5 - 200 \mu m$. In the $3 - 40 \mu m$ range, fibre filters especially are more efficient than wire gauze.

— The filters can be easily cleaned by applying high pressure, superheated steam, chemicals or by burning out.

Bronze filters have a smaller pressure loss than high grade steel filters under similar conditions and having the same dimensions since both are made from almost spherical particle powders. The heat resistance, strength and, up to a point, the chemical resistance of high grade steel filters is superior to that of bronze filters. Bronze filters are, however, more economical because they are so easy to make by vibration sintering.

Filter elements made from interlinked CrNi fibres in mat form require a support to give them the necessary rigidity because of their thinness. They therefore have a very small pressure loss. The porosity of these materials ranges from 80 to 90 % and the pores are all open, so that filtration efficiency is great.

Applications

Sintered filters are suitable for filtering, separation, throttling, dispersing, drying, moistening, conveying and storing.

Filtration means keeping back solid particles in a flowing liquid or gas. The characteristic feature of sintered filters is that filtration occurs deep inside the pore labyrinth. The filtration effect may be divided into:
- screening (large particles),
- impact effect (medium size particles) and
- adhesion (small particles).

The separation rate of such a filter with its large volume of pores is far higher than that of a screen with the same mesh width, i. e. even at the given nominal pore width of the filter, far smaller particles are retained in the filter's pore system. The adhesion of the particles to the pore walls and the deflection of the lipuid stream (impact effect) so that particles can be deposited at points where there is reduced flow rate, enable large amounts of contaminant particles to be retained by the filter.

The labyrinthine character of the pore system, i. e. the impact and adhesion effects inside the pores make it possible to separate liquids with different surface tensions such as water and oil or of liquids and gases such as the separation of aerosols from gases.

The deflection of flow lines of a medium inside the pore labyrinth has a throttling effect. Uneven speeds, i. e. pressure surges and fluctuations are compensated and damped. Applications include the protection of sensitive measuring instruments and pipe systems against shock, sound insulation of compressed air and steam, and protection against flame strike-back.

Sintered filters are used for mixing, dispersing and homogenising gases, liquids as well as polymer melts of different colours, compositions or temperatures. Another example is the introduction of superheated steam to heat up liquids. Here, the sintered filter reduces the pressure and finely disperses the steam, thereby preventing sudden surges of steam.

Filter plates, trays and channels are widely used in tanks, silos and transport vehicles to dry, moisten and store powdered and granular materials.

Cleaning of filters, screens and extruder parts in the fluidised bed
Horst Uhrner

In all continuous plastics processing operations, especially extrusion, great efforts are made to maintain constant processing conditions. This has led to the development of improved — but also more expensive — designs of material feed, polymer melt filtration and pelletising units, but has also contributed towards making such parts as screws, breaker plates, screens, filters and extrusion dies easier to clean.

Methods of cleaning

Until now, parts have been cleaned by incineration, using an open flame, or mechanically (e. g. for PVC), depending on the type of polymer. These methods however have several disadvantages which are listed below:

a) *Incineration*

    the parts are heated unevenly as well as being overheated

    distortion, loss of hardness, risk of scaling

    incomplete removal of polymer residues

    smoke and fume nuisance

    excessively high MAC at the place of work

b) *Mechanical cleaning*

    damage to surfaces and edges

    incomplete removal of polymer residues

    risk to dimensional stability

    expensive to operate

    cumbersome and labour-intensive

    a lengthy process.

Cleaning techniques now in use

a) *Thermal methods*
   incinerating furnace
   salt bath
   vacuum oven
   fluidised bed

b) *Chemical methods*
   glycol baths or other solvents

c) *Cleaning compounds*

Fig. 1. Fluidised bed cleaning unit.

The removal of unwanted polymer residues from metal surfaces by oxidation is a technique used for many years, employing either special incinerating furnaces or salt baths. The parts to be cleaned are heated to about 400 – 450 °C in the furnace or by immersing them in a hot salt melt. The oxygen present initiated oxidation and carbonisation, thereby removing the organic substances from the metal surfaces. The advantage of these methods is their universal applicability, irrespective of the type of polymer to be removed. The disadvantage is that the exothermic cleaning process is difficult to control. Overheating of the metal parts cannot be prevented, especially when using the furnace method, and if one is using the salt bath process, there are also certain corrosion problems, as well as difficulties in removing residual salts and emissions.

The fluidised bed cleaning bath

The fluidised bed cleaning process has been used for about 15 years for removing polymer residues from machine components. The actual cleaning bath, fig. 1, consists of a retort accomodated in an insulated housing and filled with granular aluminium oxide with a particle size of about 0,1 mm. The bottom of the retort consists of a diffusion plate through which compressed air is blown.

The cleaning operation

The cleaning process is shown schematically in fig. 2. The dirty metal parts are placed into a basket or, in the case of heavy parts, suspended underneath

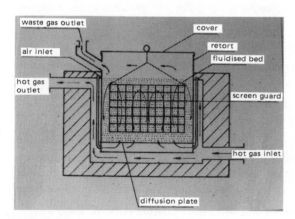

Fig. 2. Schematic diagram showing the cleaning process.

the lid. The basket is then lowered into the retort by means of lifting gear. The hot aluminium oxide particles quickly and evenly heat up the charge to the required $400 - 460\,^{\circ}C$, at which temperature the atmospheric oxygen converts all organic constituents of the polymer into gaseous products. The most important aspects in the cleaning of complex and expensive metal parts by this technique are:

1. Even heating, without accompanying distortion, of parts assembled from a number of components, e. g. melt pumps, die heads, slot dies etc.

2. Supplying the amount of oxygen necessary to achieve fast but controlled conversion of the polymer residues.

3. The fluidised bed medium directly absorbs the extra heat produced during the cleaning process, removes this from the metal parts and thereby ensures accurate heating.

4. The fluidised bed medium is not used up, is completely inert and in no way affects the operator.

Cleaning by the fluidised bed method takes between 30 minutes and about 3 hours. A screen taken from a screen changer for example, will be clean after $30 - 50$ minutes. A blown film die assembled from various components, or a compact slit die, require several hours for cleaning.

The complete plant

Apart from the fluidised bed cleaning bath, other components are necessary in order to produce an effective system. The minimum equipment required is as follows:

the fluidised bed cleaning bath;

lifting gear, charging basket, table to accomodate the metal parts before and after cleaning;

extraction unit, waste air line with fresh air bypass and a solid particle separator.

In Germany as well as many other European countries there are extensive laws and regulations to protect the environment and limit the amounts of toxic substances discharged into the atmosphere. In the case of the fluidised bed this means that the vapours produced must be burnt off in a special unit.

Although fluidised bed cleaning baths had hitherto been exclusively heated electrically, there has been a change in thinking. Now, the waste heat produced by burning the vapours is used to heat the cleaning bath, the energy being composed of the flame of the burner and the calorific value of the gases.

If the hot waste gases are passed into the double jacket of the retort, the fluidised bed is heated without the use of electrical energy. Any desired temperature can be set with great accuracy by means of simple control instruments. At the same time the temperature of the waste air is lowered so that it can be passed into the atmosphere without the use of specially high chimneys or other reservations. The residual heat is available to the operator who can use it to make steam or hot water, to heat oil etc.

Another step towards saving energy is the combustion of plastics wastes in the fluidised bed. In large plants it is worthwhile to invest in a second, smaller fluidised bed which is fed continuously with waste moulding compound, powder or other polymer waste. This produces a constant stream of waste gas which is then passed into the combustion unit.

Fluidised bed cleaning is not only suitable for large plants but can also be used as a means of cleaning in a repair shop. The savings that can be achieved, coupled with the advantages such as reduced wear on tools, simpler operation, improved hygienic conditions at the place of work, prevention of harmful emissions, make this a good investment.

Emissions and methods of approval

Authorising bodies are working with increasingly less discretionary latitude and are continually reducing permissible residual concentrations. The Federal Emission Law clearly states:

Plants designed to completely or partly eliminate solid or liquid substances through incineration or thermal decomposition or which have been designed to recover certain constituents through combustion of solid substances, must have official approval for their operation

The waste air produced in any incineration or combustion process must be subsequently burnt. The same apllies to the contamination of waterways where a special purification unit must be used, depending on the type of contamination present in the water.

The approval procedure for such plants is not concerned with size or capacity. The operator must make an application, which is then examined by the official authorities.

Plant manufacturers can give considerable help to intending users of their equipment in getting the necessary approval from the authorities by providing detailed technical data proving that the regulations concerning atmospheric pollution can be strictly adhered to.

Conclusions

Nearly all metal parts, including those made from non-ferrous metals, can be effectively and gently cleaned by the fluidised bed process, provided they will withstand temperatures of between 400 and 460 °C, irrespective of the type of polymer residue to be removed. Small units as well as large plants can be operated economically, depending on the type of application and capacity.

Considerable advantages result for the operators as regards handling and hygiene at the place of work.

Bibliography

Dr. Ken Steffin – Procedyne Corp.: "Cleaning plastics processing hardware" Plastics machinery and equipment – May 1977.

Bayard Baldridge – Lewis Corp. and Charles Sears – Procedyne Corp.: "Spinnerette Cleaning" Fiber Producer April 1978.

H. Uhrner – Schwing GmbH: "Entlacken in der Wirbelschicht" Pulver u. Lack – No. 2/1981.

H. Uhrner – Schwing GmbH: "Reinigung von Werkzeugteilen im Wirbelbett" Synthetic – No. 7/1981.

Cleaning of plastics and rubber contaminated machine parts

Hans-Otto Strohschein

There are various methods for cleaning plastics and rubber contaminated components. The advantage of the cleaning device discussed in this paper over other devices and systems lies in its mode of action. Since energy, labour and other costs are rising rapidly at the moment, the choice of the most suitable and most economical cleaning system is of far-reaching importance. The advantages of the system include:

nearly all polymers and rubber compounds can be removed from metal parts by vacuum pyrolysis, i. e. the decomposition of chemical compounds at high temperatures;

the parts to be cleaned are subjected to a minimum of movement;

no burning;

minimal environmental pollution;

energy-saving cleaning;

parts to be treated can be cleaned effectively yet gently, without damage to the surface.

Method of operation

A cleaning device must be able to remove all traces of thermoplastics, thermosets and rubber from extrusion dies and injection moulds economically and effectively. Inexpert cleaning methods such as burning off with a blow torch or scraping with a knife require a lot of time and are usually inefficient, as well as involving the risk of mechanical damage or local overheating, making the component unusable.

Cleaning devices hitherto used, e. g. hot air ovens, salt baths and aluminium oxide units incinerate the polymer. This new device, on the other hand, removes these residues primarily through melting.

Fig. 1 is a schematic drawing of the process. The parts to be cleaned are placed inside the cleaning chamber which is then sealed so that it is vacuum-tight. The chamber is then heated to about 480 °C and at the same time

209

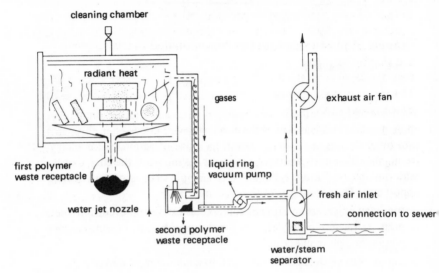

process flow diagram

cleaning chamber

radiant heat

gases

exhaust air fan

first polymer
waste receptacle

liquid ring
vacuum pump

fresh air inlet

connection to sewer

water jet nozzle

second polymer
waste receptacle

water/steam
separator

Fig. 1. Cleaning unit for polymer contaminated parts – schematic drawing.

Fig. 2. Cleaning unit for polymer contaminated parts, model Beringer 1724.

210

evacuated using a liquid-ring vacuum-pump. The polymer melts, disintegrates and partially vaporises at this temperature, the melted plastic being collected in suitable receptacles. The polymer vapours are condensed in water jet units which can be either upstram or downstream from the vacuum pump, and are then separated, the gases being led off through waste air exhaust fans. The water from the liquid-ring pump is passed into the sewer system. To keep water consumption down to a minimum, it is possible to install a closed water circuit.

Fig. 2 shows the cleaning unit with the carriage for the parts to be treated retracted. Dirtied parts are placed on this carriage with the biggest opening facing downwards. Inside the heating chamber one can see the heating coils. The fully loaded carriage is now moved into the heating chamber, fig. 3, which is made vacuum tight with clamps. The control desk is equipped with a temperature pre-selection system, vacuum gauge and a cleaning cycle counter.

On pressing the start button, the heaters are switched on and the liquid-ring pump produces the vacuum. After the pre-set temperature has been reached, this is kept constant by means of thermocouples. When the pre-set cleaning period has been completed, the plant switches itself off, although the pump

Fig. 3. Introduction of contaminated parts into the cleaning chamber.

continues to function for a short while in order to exhaust gases which continue to be formed. If the pump should break down for any reason during operation, the heating system is automatically switched off. If excess pressure develops inside the heating chamber, this can be quite easily adjusted by means of a flap valve. By far the greater part of the polymer is melted and caught in the first waste receptacle. The remaining polymer residues are vaporised and eliminated in a second stage of the process. Most cleaning cycles last 60–90 minutes, depending on the number of parts to be cleaned and the amount of polymer which has to be heated up. This results in the following advantages:

the possibility of removing many different kinds of polymer,

very fast cleaning,

simple operation.

Cleaning effect

Parts contaminated with PA, PE or PUR are treated for 60 minutes at 450 °C and at a vacuum of 673 Torr. Fig. 4 shows PA dirtied components before treatment, fig. 5 the same parts after treatment. Parts contaminated with PVC are cleaned for 50 minutes at 440 °C and 673 Torr vacuum. During

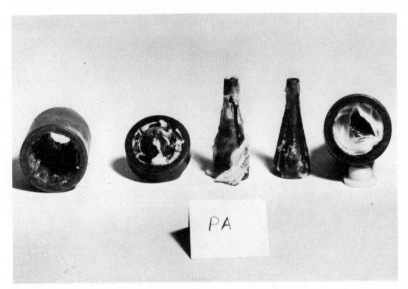

Fig. 4. PA contaminated parts before cleaning.

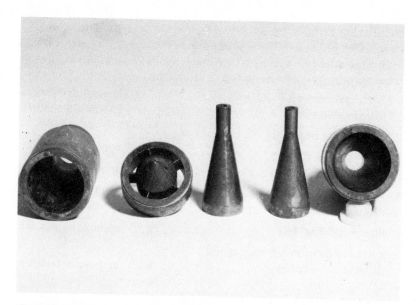

Fig. 5. The parts shown in fig. 4, after cleaning.

this treatment, the PVC is converted into ash which covers the surface as a film but which can be removed by means of a jet of compressed air. After sandblasting and greasing with silicone fluid, the clean parts can once again be used.

Waste gases

The vapours produced during cleaning are almost completely condensed in water jet units and passed into the sewage system. It is not necessary to use additional decontamination equipment.

Time required

Comparison of the process under actual production conditions with conventional cleaning methods gave the following information:

The time required to clean components by the above method, including putting in and taking out of the heating chamber, application of compressed air with subsequent sandblasting was about 20 minutes (excluding the time spent inside the heating chamber). Below we give details of the time required for the method used so far.

213

1. RAUPID pot screens (PVC)
   a) loosen dirt in screen (different mesh sizes)
   b) clean screen
   c) sandblasting
      70 mm diameter . . . . approx. 25 minutes
      106 mm diameter . . . . approx. 35 minutes

2. Intermediate ring ϕ 70 (PS), burning out,
   sandblasting . . . . approx. 10 minutes

3. Flat screen ϕ 70 (PVC) . . . . approx. 10 minutes

4. 70 structure (plast. PVC) burning out,
   sandblasting . . . . approx. 10 minutes

5. Flange coupling (PE) . . . . approx. 10 minutes

6. Sperical structure (PE) burning out,
   cleaning, sandblasting) . . . . approx. 20 minutes

Total time for all parts . . . . approx. 120 minutes

This means that there is a time saving of 100 minutes.

Another point worth mentioning is that with the conventional method of cleaning, there is the risk that the parts being cleaned are damaged or even made useless through inexpert treatment.

Types of cleaning units

These cleaning units are made in four different sizes, whose measurements are shown in fig. 6. Special models are supplied for cleaning polymer contaminated extruder or injection moulding screws, fig. 7.

For rubber contamined parts or end products which are classed as rejects and from which one wants to recover the steel core, one uses a special rubber cleaning unit. This resembles the device used to remove thermoplastics but is equipped with two extra screens, fig. 8. The operating temperature is around 400 °C. Test results have shown that considerable amounts of hydrocarbon gases are emitted during the cleaning process, amounting to about 25—45 % of the weight of rubber, depending on such factors as rubber compound formulation, cycle time, temperature as well as the size of the cleaning unit. The remaining rubber stays behind in the oven in the form of ash, or in the collecting tank in the form of oil.

214

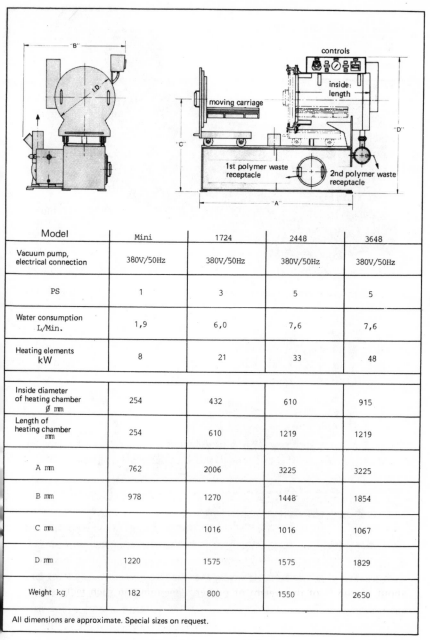

Model	Mini	1724	2448	3648
Vacuum pump, electrical connection	380V/50Hz	380V/50Hz	380V/50Hz	380V/50Hz
PS	1	3	5	5
Water consumption L/Min.	1,9	6,0	7,6	7,6
Heating elements kW	8	21	33	48
Inside diameter of heating chamber Ø mm	254	432	610	915
Length of heating chamber mm	254	610	1219	1219
A mm	762	2006	3225	3225
B mm	978	1270	1448	1854
C mm		1016	1016	1067
D mm	1220	1575	1575	1829
Weight kg	182	800	1550	2650

All dimensions are approximate. Special sizes on request.

Fig. 6. Dimensions of cleaning units.

Fig. 7. Cleaning unit for extruder screws.

Fig. 8. Cleaning unit for rubber contaminated parts.

216

For many kinds of application, this high proportion of hydrocarbon gas could be too much. In this case, the incorporation of an after-burner will greatly reduce the amount of gas emitted into the atmosphere. Other gases are produced only in small amounts so that they do not present an environmental problem. The number of macro-particles produced was so small in all the tests, that these can be ignored.

Fig. 9 illustrates the recovery of the steel carcase from a rubber covered anti-vibration pad, so that it can be re-covered with rubber. No waste respectacles are needed for the rubber cleaner since the metal carcase, covered in ash, lies on the carriage as it slides out of the oven. This ash can then be knocked off or shaken out. Whether or not the use of an after-burner is necessary will depend on local authorities. All the units in operation in Germany have so far been used without after-burners. An environmental protection study has been prepared, but is too extensive to be discussed here.

Fig. 9. Rubber covered anti-vibration pad, before and after cleaning.

Authors

Albano-Müller   Dr.-Ing. Lothar
Sintermetallwerk Krebsöge GmbH
Postfach 5100 · D-5608 Radevormwald
Tel. (02191) 693241 · FS 8513803

Anders   Ing. (grad.) Dietmar VDI
Hermann Berstorff Maschinenbau GmbH
Postfach 629 · D-3000 Hannover 1
Tel. (0511) 5702320 · FS 921348

Bauer   Dr.-Ing. Wolfgang
BASF AG, Abt. D-DET/KA, I 522
D-6700 Ludwigshafen
Tel. (0621) 603442 · FS 464758

Bevis   Prof. Dr.-Ing. Michael J.
Brunel University
Department of Non-Metallic Materials
GB-Uxbridge · Middlesex UB 8 3 PH
Tel. (895) 37188

Ehrmann   Dr.-Ing. Gerd
BASF AG, Abt. D-DET/KA, I 522
D-6700 Ludwigshafen
Tel. (0621) 603442 · FS 464758

Hensen   Prof. Dr.-Ing. Friedhelm
Barmag Barmer Maschinenfabrik AG
Postfach 110240 · D-5630 Remscheid 11
Tel. (02191) 609346 · FS 8513611

Herbener	Ing. Albert Bolton Emerson S.A. Postfach 2333 · CH-1003 Lausanne Tel. (021) 206451 · FS 24308
Köching	Ing. Horst J. Kreyenborg & Co. Postfach 156030 · D-4400 Münster Tel. (0251) 211021 · FS 892667
Lambertus	Ing. (grad.) Friedrich Werner & Pfleiderer Postfach 301220 · D-7000 Stuttgart 30 Tel. (0711) 8956632 · FS 722696
Masberg	Dipl.-Ing. Ullrich VDI Institut für Kunststoffverarbeitung, Abt. Extrusion Pontstraße 49 · D-5100 Aachen Tel. (0241) 803884 · FS 832358
Pahl	Prof. Dr.-Ing. Manfred VDI Universität – GHS Paderborn FB 10 – Mech. Verfahrenstechnik Pohlweg 55 · D-4790 Paderborn Tel. (05251) 602364 · FS 936776
Röhlig	Ing. Rainer VDI Sintermetallwerk Krebsöge GmbH Postfach 5100 · D-5608 Radevormwald 1 Tel. (02191) 693241 · FS 8513803
Schneider	Dr.-Ing. Wolfgang BASF AG, Abt. D-DET/KA, I·522 D-6700 Ludwigshafen Tel. (0621) 603442 · FS 464758
Siemens	Werner Werner E. Siemens Verfahrenstechnik Krautsander Hafenstraße 2 · D-2168 Drochtersen Tel. (04143) 7242

Schönbauer	Dip.-Ing. Dr. mont. Gerhard Haver & Boecker Postfach 33 20 · D-4740 Oelde 1 Tel. (02522) 30256 · FS 89521
Strohschein	Ing. (grad.) Hans-Otto Hernball KG Sandtorquai 5 · D-2000 Hamburg 11 Tel. (040) 364691 · FS 213661
Uhland	Dr.-Ing. Eberhard Hermann Berstorff Maschinenbau GmbH Postfach 629 · D-3000 Hannover 1 Tel. (0511) 5702435 · FS 921348
Uhrner	Ing. Horst Schwing Verfahrenstechnik GmbH Postfach 219 , D-4133 Neukirchen-Vl. 2 Tel. (02845) 3031 · FS 8121237